FANTASTIC
BRAIN
GAMES

First published by Parragon in 2008

Parragon
Queen Street House
4 Queen Street
Bath BA1 1HE, UK

ISBN: 978-1-4075-3506-7

Created and Produced by David Etherington Design
www.davidetheringtondesign.com

Design: David Etherington, Luke Griffin

Printed in China

FANTASTIC BRAIN GAMES

GUY CAMPBELL
PAUL MORAN

PaRragon

Bath · New York · Singapore · Hong Kong · Cologne · Delhi · Melbourne

INTRODUCTION

We often take our brains for granted, forgetting that they would benefit from a good work out just like any other part of our body – and this book is designed to provide just that. All you need is some pencils, paper and a quiet corner and that will be the last anyone will hear from you in the next few weeks as you put your brain through its paces.

Fantastic Brain Games is a fun and enjoyable way to exercise the mind for peak mental fitness, as it gives you a thorough cerebral work out through a variety of puzzles including logic tests, number games, picture puzzles and lateral thinking riddles.

In addition to these intellectual exercises, many of the puzzle entries come complete with a fascinating fact from the fields of arts, history and science, and an accompanying quote to inform and inspire you. The authors of these words of wisdom are philosophers, scientists, writers and some of the greatest minds from history including Aristotle, Oscar Wilde, Samuel Johnson and Thomas Jefferson to name but a few.

So in the pages ahead, tackle the puzzles, study the facts and be inspired by the quotes – and then reap the rewards of an exercised and mentally agile mind.

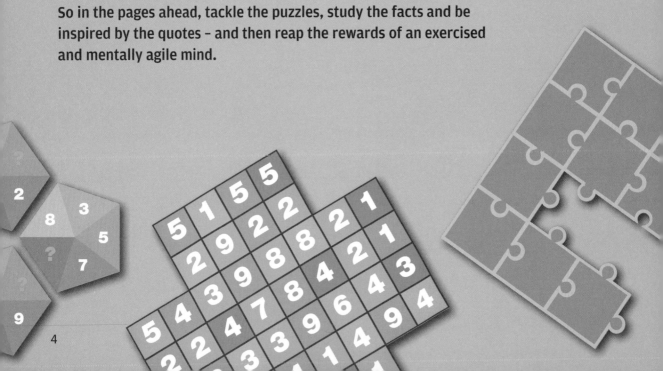

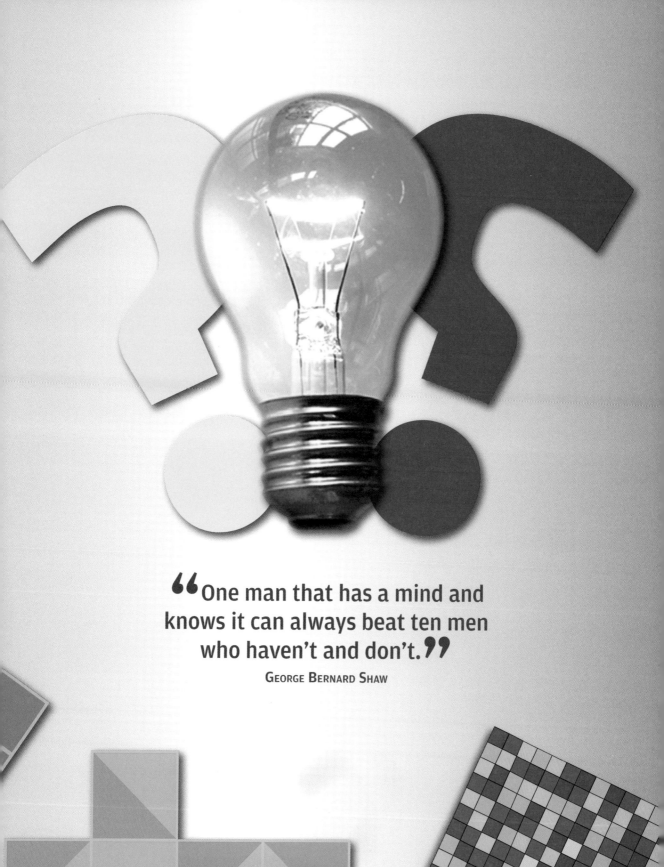

"One man that has a mind and knows it can always beat ten men who haven't and don't."

GEORGE BERNARD SHAW

HOW TO USE THIS BOOK

Fantastic Brain Games is uniquely devised to give you the complete mental workout, providing challenging puzzles, as well as fascinating facts and interesting quotes to inform and inspire.

Puzzle number This book contains 179 puzzles and brainteasers, designed to put your mind through its paces.

Items you will need Some puzzles may require some basic equipment and these are listed here.

- PEN
- PAPER
- RULER
- COLOURED PENS

Difficulty This gauge will inform you of the difficulty of each puzzle. 'Easy' puzzles may take only a matter of minutes to complete while those listed as 'Hard' may take rather more time.

EASY   MEDIUM   HARD

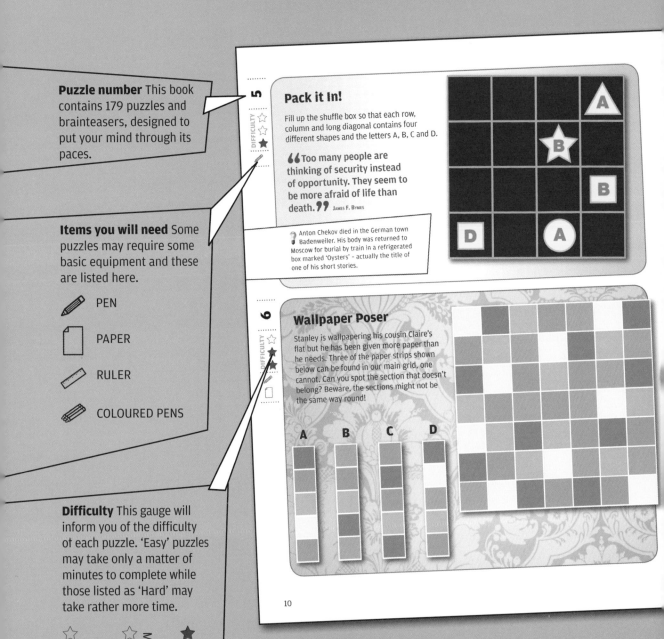

5

DIFFICULTY

Pack it In!

Fill up the shuffle box so that each row, column and long diagonal contains four different shapes and the letters A, B, C and D.

❝Too many people are thinking of security instead of opportunity. They seem to be more afraid of life than death.❞ James F. Bymes

Anton Chekov died in the German town Badenweiler. His body was returned to Moscow for burial by train in a refrigerated box marked 'Oysters' - actually the title of one of his short stories.

6

DIFFICULTY

Wallpaper Poser

Stanley is wallpapering his cousin Claire's flat but he has been given more paper than he needs. Three of the paper strips shown below can be found in our main grid, one cannot. Can you spot the section that doesn't belong? Beware, the sections might not be the same way round!

A   B   C   D

10

Solutions

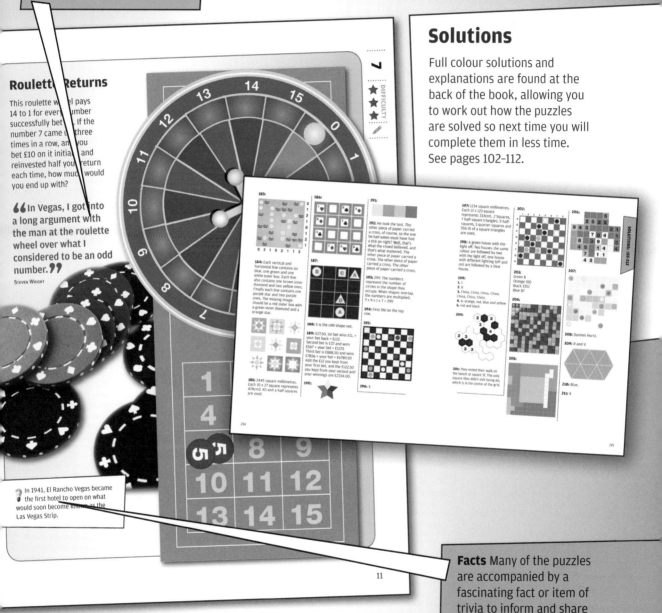

Roulette Returns

This roulette wheel pays 14 to 1 for every number successfully bet on. If the number 7 came up three times in a row, and you bet £10 on it initially and reinvested half your return each time, how much would you end up with?

66 In Vegas, I got into a long argument with the man at the roulette wheel over what I considered to be an odd number. **99**

STEVEN WRIGHT

In 1941, El Rancho Vegas became the first hotel to open on what would soon become known as the Las Vegas Strip.

7

★★★ DIFFICULTY

Bees and Blooms

Every bloom has one bee found horizontally or vertically adjacent to it. No bee can be in an adjacent square to another bee (even diagonally). The numbers by each row and column tell you how many bees are there. Can you locate all the bees?

BLOOM   **BEE**

 A productive queen bee surrounded by efficient drones can lay between 2,000-3,000 eggs every day.

Beautiful Boxes

Which of the four boxed figures completes the set?

66 If I keep a green bough in my heart, then the singing bird will come. **99** CHINESE PROVERB

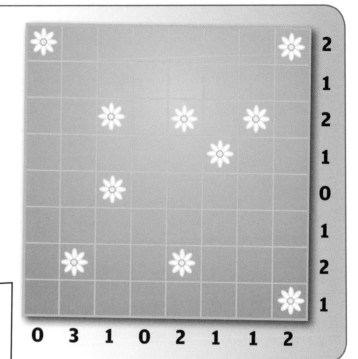

A hummingbird feeds up to 15 times every hour in order to remain active enough to maintain a body temperature of 105-109°F.

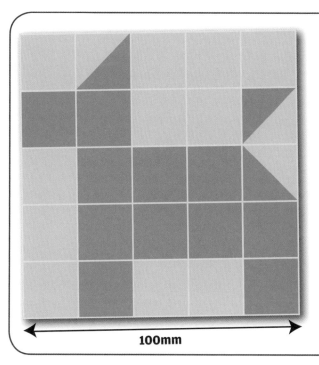

Gone to the Dogs

Can you work out the approximate area of this picture that the dog image takes up?

66 Scratch a dog and you'll find a permanent job. **99**

FRANKLIN P. JONES

100mm

3

☆
☆
★ DIFFICULTY

According to Herodotus, when a dog died in an Egyptian household the entire family went into mourning and shaved their heads and bodies in memory of the animal.

Play the Cards

Fill up the shuffle box so that each row, column and long diagonal contains a Jack, Queen, King and Ace of each suita.

66 A lot of life is dealing with your curse, dealing with the cards you were given that aren't so nice. Does it make you into a monster, or can you temper it in some way, or accept it and go in some other direction? **99**

WES CRAVEN

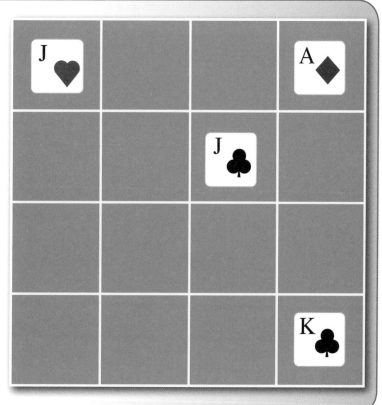

4

☆
★ DIFFICULTY
★

DIFFICULTY ☆ ☆ ★ ✏

Pack it In!

Fill up the shuffle box so that each row, column and long diagonal contains four different shapes and the letters A, B, C and D.

❝Too many people are thinking of security instead of opportunity. They seem to be more afraid of life than death.❞ James F. Bymes

💡 Anton Chekov died in the German town Badenweiler. His body was returned to Moscow for burial by train in a refrigerated box marked 'Oysters' – actually the title of one of his short stories.

DIFFICULTY ☆ ★ ★ ✏ 🗅

Wallpaper Poser

Stanley is wallpapering his cousin Claire's flat but he has been given more paper than he needs. Three of the paper strips shown below can be found in our main grid, one cannot. Can you spot the section that doesn't belong? Beware, the sections might not be the same way round!

A   **B**   **C**   **D**

Roulette Returns

This roulette wheel pays 14 to 1 for every number successfully bet on. If the number 7 came up three times in a row, and you bet £10 on it initially and reinvested half your return each time, how much would you end up with?

> **In Vegas, I got into a long argument with the man at the roulette wheel over what I considered to be an odd number.**
> STEVEN WRIGHT

In 1941, El Rancho Vegas became the first hotel to open on what would soon become known as the Las Vegas Strip.

Galaxy of Stars

Believe it or not, none of these stars are exactly alike. They represent every single combination of five colours – except one. Can you work out the colour placements on the missing star?

In 1958, Perry Como received the first official Gold Record for his recording of *Catch a Falling Star*.

Colour to Come

One of our swatches is missing! Can you work out the four colour sequence that completes the set?

❝The habit of looking on the bright side of every event is worth more than a thousand pounds a year.❞ SAMUEL JOHNSON

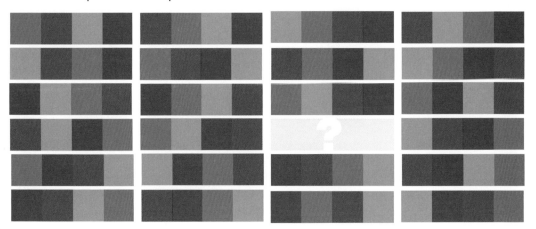

Romantic Riddle

Princess Penelope fell in love with a lowly woodcutter called Frank. The people were delighted that the princess had chosen one of them for her beau. Her father the King, on the other hand, was distraught at his daughter's terrible choice in eligible boys, and he cooked up a plan to get Frank out of the picture.

"We must let fate decide", he said "whether this commoner can claim my daughter and my crown. If the gods smile on him, I will do the same."

The people thought this was fair enough, and the test of fate was designed thus: On two pieces of paper were drawn a cross and a tick. The pieces of paper would be placed in a bag and Frank would pick. If he chose the tick, Penelope was his. If he chose the cross, he must leave the kingdom forever... The test was set for Saturday morning at 11 o'clock, and the whole kingdom would turn out to watch.

On Friday night, very late, Frank answered his door to a friend, Bob, who worked in the Palace kitchens. Bob, taking the Queen her nightly cocoa, had overheard the King telling her that both pieces of paper would have crosses on them!

"What am I going to do?" said Frank. "If I do the test I'll lose and be banished. If I don't I'll never marry Penelope... And if I expose the King in front of everyone he'll surely have me killed!" Exactly what did Frank do to keep his head, and his bride?

> **At the touch of love everyone becomes a poet.**
> PLATO

The Brothers Grimm, Jakob and Wilhelm, began collecting and writing fairy tales from 1807. They were depicted on the German 100 Deutsche Mark from 1990 until the introduction of the Euro in 2000.

Shape Stacker

Can you work out the logic behind the numbers in these shapes, and what number should replace the question mark?

❝How can a woman be expected to be happy with a man who insists on treating her as if she were a perfectly normal human being.❞ OSCAR WILDE

💡 In 2004 scientists in Arizona discovered that women are capable of seeing more subtle shades of red than men.

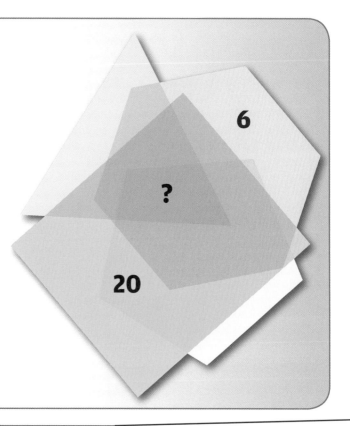

The One and Only

Only one of the tiles below is unique, the other 14 all have an exact double. Can you find the one-off?

💡 The Catalan architect Antoni Gaudí transformed Barcelona, Spain, into a mosaic city in the early 1990s. He used recycled tiles to create his outdoor works of art.

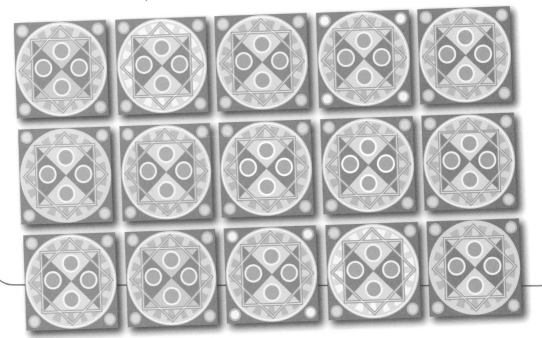

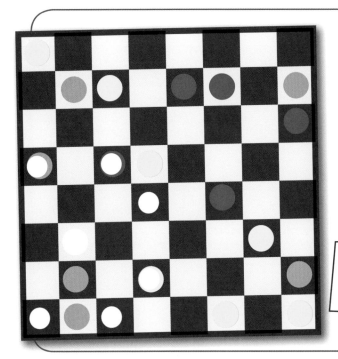

Knight's Move

Find an empty square in the grid that is one chess knight's move away from a blue, red and yellow circle. A knight's move is an 'L' shape – two squares sideways, up or down in any direction, followed by one square to the left or right.

❝Architecture begins where engineering ends.❞

WALTER GROPIUS

💡 Excavation work on the 51-mile long Panama Canal began in 1904. The first ship entered the waterway ten years later in 1914.

Shaping Relations

By examining the relationships of the following shapes, can you identify the next shape?

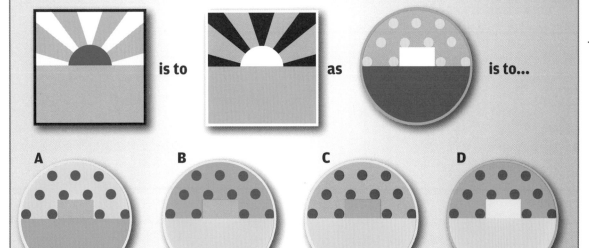

is to ... as ... is to...

A   **B**   **C**   **D**

 Andy Warhol was actually born Andrew Warhola in Pittsburgh, Pennsylvania, in 1928.

Love is in the Area

Can you work out the approximate area that the happy couple are occupying?

"To love is to find pleasure in the happiness of the person loved. "

ANONYMOUS

100mm

Las Vegas, Nevada, is known as the "Wedding Capital of the World" with an average of 150 couples getting married there every day.

Tricky Terrace

The sequence of terraced houses below follows a logical pattern. Can you work out what colour house follows, and whether the light should be on?

The Kremlin in Moscow has been the official residence of the Russian ruler since the capital was reestablished there in 1918 by Lenin. The word means 'fortress.'

"Houses are built to live in, and not to look on: therefore let use be preferred before uniformity. " FRANCIS BACON

Flag Flummox

Study these flags for a minute, then cover with a sheet of paper and answer the five questions below.

"If you want a symbolic gesture, don't burn the flag; wash it."

NORMAN THOMAS

Questions:

1. How many flags contain the colour blue? 2. How many flags do not contain the colour red? 3. Which flag is between two crosses? 4. How many make up the three top row flags? 5. Which two colours only feature on one flag each?

Spiderweb

The numbers in some cells in the spiderweb indicate the exact number of black cells that should border it. Shade these black, until all the numbers are surrounded by the correct number of black cells.

"The bird a nest, the spider a web, man friendship."

WILLIAM BLAKE

The Brazilian wandering spider is thought to be the most venomous in the world. It is native to South and Central America but was first discovered in the Pantanal, Brazil.

Park Life

Jack and Sadie met at the snack stand by the fountain before taking a long rambling walk around the park, the directions of which are below. Eventually, they stopped to rest on a bench. Which bench? And what is the only square on the map they didn't visit?

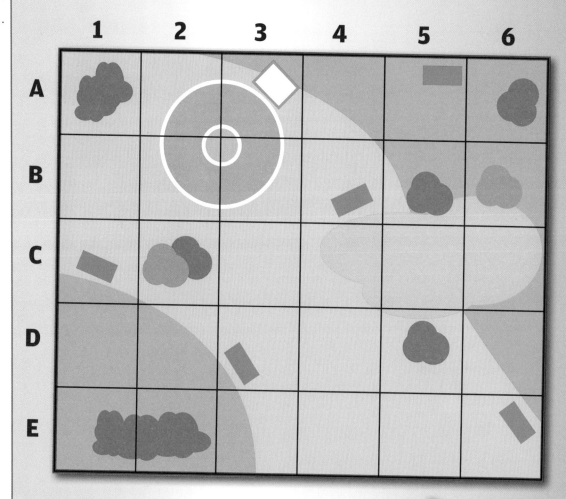

3E, 3S, 5W, 2E, 2N, 1S, 2S, 2W, 5E, 4W, 4N, 1W, 4E, 1W, 4S, 1E, 1N, 3W, 2E, 1N, 2W, 1W, 4E, 1N, 4W, 3E, 1W, 3W, 1S.

Rome's Trevi fountain was designed by Nicola Salvi, who died in 1751 when the project was only half complete. It was finally finished in 1762.

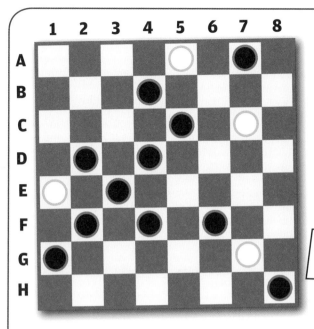

	1	2	3	4	5	6	7	8
A								
B								
C								
D								
E								
F								
G								
H								

Checkers

Make a move for white so that eight black pieces are left, none of which are in the same column or row.

66Courage is like love; it must have hope for nourishment.99

NAPOLEON BONAPARTE

In 1937, Austria became the first country to issue a special commemorative stamp for the Christmas season.

Number Knights

These symbols represent the numbers 1 to 4. Can you work out what colour knights are representing which numbers and make a working sum?

66A true knight is fuller of bravery in the midst, than in the beginning of danger.99

SIR PHILIP SIDNEY

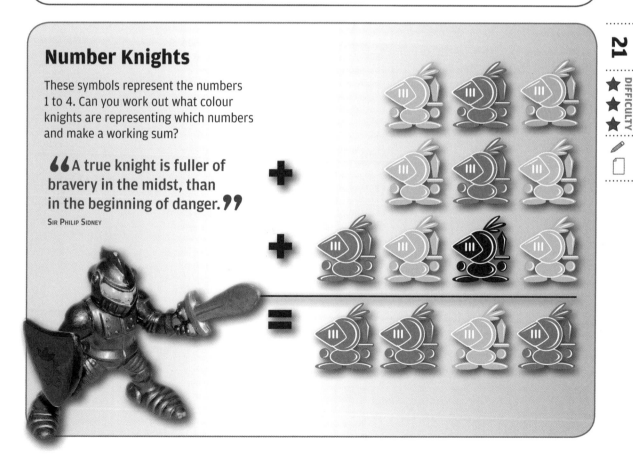

Colour Amaze

Find a path from one white cell to the other the shortest way. You may only pass from a red cell to a blue one, a blue to a yellow, a yellow to a green or a green to a red.

66 It is the artist's business to create sunshine when the sun fails. 99 ROMAIN ROLLAND

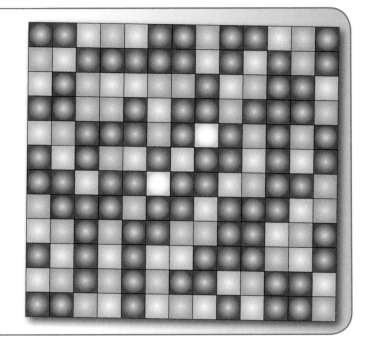

Pond and Patio

Below is a fish pond, with a surround waiting to be paved. Can you fit the pieces together and finish the job?

66 Fish say, they have their stream and pond; But is there anything beyond? 99 RUPERT BROOKE

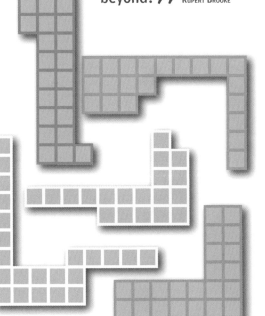

Number Chunks

Divide up the grid into four equally sized, equally shaped parts, each containing numbers that add up to 50.

> ❝Anyone who thinks there's safety in numbers hasn't looked at the stock market pages.❞
>
> IRENE PETER

Grid:

```
        5  1  5  5
        2  9  2  2
5  4  3  9  8  8  2  1
2  2  4  7  8  4  2  1
1  8  3  3  9  6  4  3
2  4  5  4  1  4  9  4
        7  8  1  1
        4  2  2  2
```

💡 Two dogs survived the sinking of the *Titanic* in 1912 – a Pomeranian belonging to a Margaret Hays of New York is listed in lifeboat 7, whilst a Pekingese accompanied Henry Sleeper Harper in number 3.

Precious Puzzler

Divide up the grid into four equally sized, equally shaped parts, each containing one of the five coloured precious gems.

> ❝The soul is placed in the body like a rough diamond, and must be polished, or the lustre of it will never appear.❞
>
> DANIEL DEFOE

💡 The Cullinan Diamond was discovered in 1905 and, at 3,106 carats, was the largest gem-quality rough diamond ever found. Cullinan I, or the Great Star of Africa - at 530 carats, formerly the largest cut diamond - was one of the 105 gems cut from it.

Back Together

These 10 pieces can be arranged to spell out the name of a famous painter... but who?

💡 It is believed that the soft drink 7-Up is so-called because its inventor Charles Leipper Grigg had previously rejected six other potential names.

Coming Together

Which two shapes below will pair up to create the top shape?

"Our life is composed greatly from dreams, from the unconscious, and they must be brought into connection with action. They must be woven together." ANAÏS NIN

💡 D. H. Lawrence's controversial 1928 novel *Lady Chatterley's Lover* was one of the top-selling books in the US upon its eventual publication in 1959. It was published in the UK in the following year. It had previously been banned in both countries because it was considered obscene.

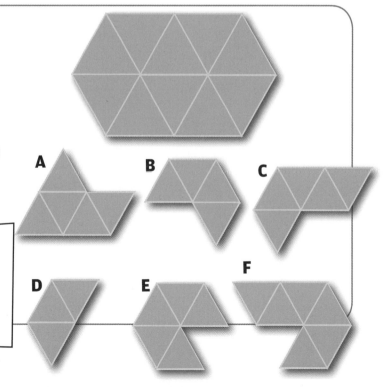

Work of Art

This wall is to be painted in green, blue and lilac, with no adjacent bricks to be in the same colour. Can you work out what colour the bottom right hand corner should be?

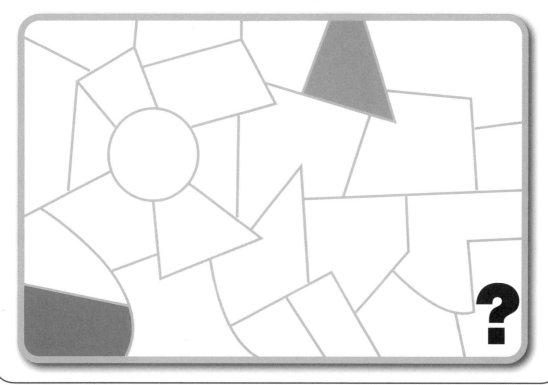

Petal Parts

Which box has exactly the right parts to make the model of the flower?

> **Life is the flower for which love is the honey.** VICTOR HUGO

A

B

C
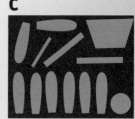

 By law, all buildings in the Moroccan city of Marrakech are painted red.

Singled Out

All the shapes in this box appear twice except one. Can you find it?

❝In questions of science, the authority of a thousand is not worth the humble reasoning of a single individual.❞ Galileo Galilei

💡 Pablo Picasso appeared as an extra in a crowd scene during Jean Cocteau's 1962 film *The Testament of Orpheus*.

Ship Shape

Only two of these naval ships are exactly the same. Can you find the matching pair?

❝We joined the Navy to see the world... And what did we see? We saw the sea.❞ Irving Berlin

💡 On 15 February 1898, the USS *Maine* sank in Havana harbour after a mystery explosion, sparking the Spanish-American War – it is the origin of the phrase "Remember the Maine!"

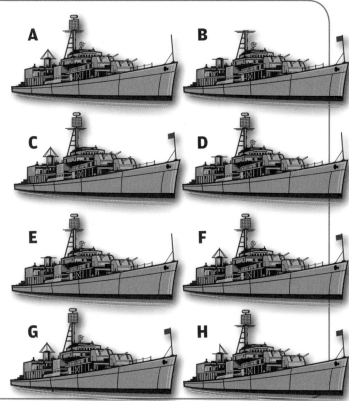

Blueprint Baffler

Look at this blueprint; can you put these shapes in order, from biggest to smallest?

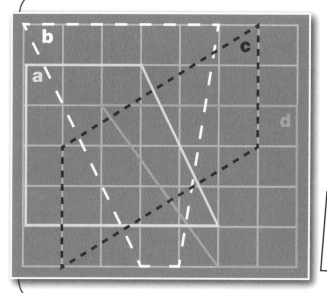

66 Happiness serves hardly any other purpose than to make unhappiness possible. 99

MARCEL PROUST

The promotional video clip that accompanied Bob Dylan's 1965 release *Subterranean Homesick Blues* was actually shot in an alleyway that runs behind the Savoy Hotel in London – where Dylan was staying.

Complete the Set

Which of the four boxed figures completes the set?

66 Being deeply learned and skilled, being well trained and using well spoken words; this is good luck. 99 HINDU PRINCE GAUTAMA SIDDHARTHA

Car giant Cadillac was named after the French explorer Antoine Laumet de La Mothe, sieur de Cadillac, who founded Detroit, Michigan, in 1701. Cadillac is a small town in the South of France near to where he was born.

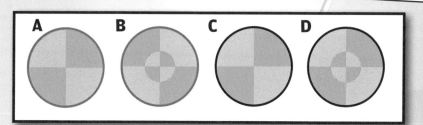

A   B   C   D

DIFFICULTY ☆ ★ ★ ✏

Scene It!

The four squares below can all be found in this jungle scene, can you track them down?

66He that does good for good's sake seeks neither paradise nor reward, but he is sure of both in the end.**99**

WILLIAM PENN

💡 Batavia was the old Dutch name for the modern Indonesian capital of Jakarta.

DIFFICULTY ★ ★ ★ 📄✏

Codoku Composer

Complete the first grid so that every row and column contains all the letters G, L, M, R, W and Y. Do the same with grid 2 and the numbers 1, 2, 3, 4, 5 and 6. To decode the finished grid, add the numbers in the shaded squares to the letters in the matching squares in the second (ie: A + 3 = D, Y + 4 = C) to get six new letters, which can be arranged to spell the name of a famous composer.

Grid 1:

L			W	R	
Y		G		W	R
			L		
W		M			
	L			Y	G
G		L	R		W

Grid 2:

4				1	3
	1	6			4
	4			2	
6		1		4	
			3		6
1	3	5			2

💡 A single manuscript page from the unpublished novella *Clisson and Eugenie*, written by Napoleon Bonaparte in 1795, fetched $35,000 at an auction in 2007.

Pentagon Puzzles

The numbers on these pentagons follow a pattern. Your task is to uncover the secret to the pattern and fill in the question marks to complete the puzzle.

In February 2004 the *New York Times* reported that 62% of all e-mail traffic could be described as 'spam'.

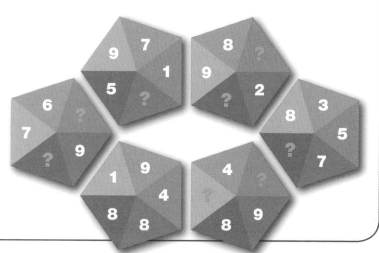

❝The greatest gift you can give another is the purity of your attention.❞ RICHARD MOSS

Centre of Attention

What numbers should replace the question mark at the centre of the second hub?

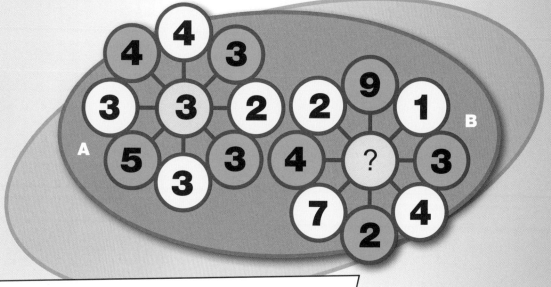

 Someone who collects money or medals is known as a numismatist.

Barnyard Balance

The pig, piglet, chicken, chick and egg each weigh an exact number between one and ten. Can you work out which number represents which, and therefore how many chicks are required to balance the final scale?

💡 Because the animals kept outgrowing the role, 30 different piglets were used during the filming of the movie *Babe* in 1995.

❝I like pigs. Dogs look up to us. Cats look down on us. Pigs treat us as equals. ❞
WINSTON CHURCHILL

Cool Question

Can you work out which areas of this diagram represent skaters that wear gloves and hats but not scarves, and people who wear gloves, hats and scarves but who don't skate?

❝Constant kindness can accomplish much. As the sun makes ice melt, kindness causes misunderstanding, mistrust, and hostility to evaporate. ❞ ALBERT SCHWEITZER

Gloves

Skaters

Scarves

A
B C D
E F G H I
J K L
M

Hats

💡 St Lidwina is the patron saint of ice skaters. Born in 1380, she lived in Holland and suffered a severe injury whilst skating as a child, from which she never recovered. She is said to have had religious visions.

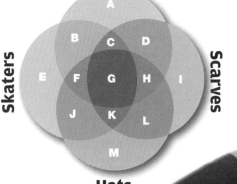

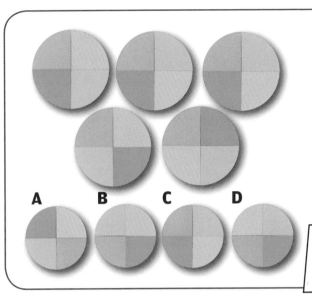

Which Wheel?

Which of the wheels: A, B, C, or D, is missing from the set above?

❝I want to die in my sleep like my grandfather... Not screaming and yelling like the passengers in his car. ❞ WILL SHRINER

💡 By 1918, 55 percent of cars in the United States were Model T Fords, which had been introduced just ten years earlier.

❝The best way to predict the future is to invent it.❞
ALAN KAY

Next in Sequence!

In the sequence below, which of the numbered alternatives, A, B, C or D, should replace the question mark?

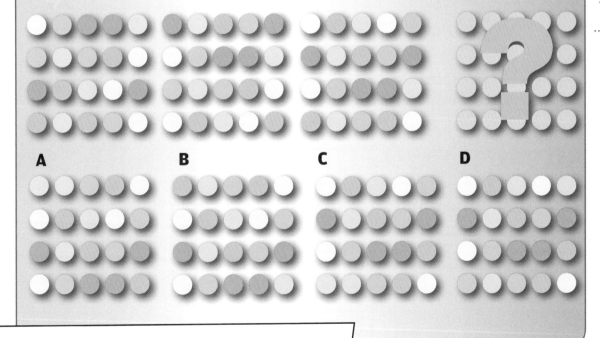

💡 Monrovia in Liberia is the only non-American capital city to be named after a US president – in this case, James Monroe.

So Much to Remember

Study these images for a minute, cover with a sheet of paper and then answer the five questions shown below.

 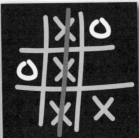  

In his experimental novel *Rayuela* or *Hopscotch*, Julio Cortazar begins by inviting readers to choose between reading the proceeding chapters in a linear or non-linear form.

Questions:

1. How many winning lines included the middle square?
2. Which section of the game grid was always empty?
3. Did X or O win the game with the black background?
4. How many bottom right-hand corners featured an 'X'?
5. How many 'O' were there altogether?

Letter Values

Work out which number is represented by which letter, and fill in the question mark.

❝I wonder if illiterate people get the full effect of alphabet soup?❞ JERRY SEINFELD

The Ottoman Empire once had seven emperors in seven months. They died of (in order): burning, choking, drowning, stabbing, heart failure, poisoning and being thrown from a horse.

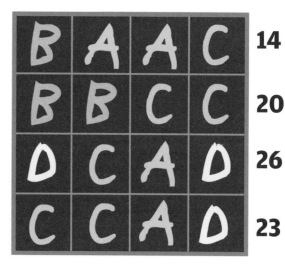

B	A	A	C	14
B	B	C	C	20
D	C	A	D	26
C	C	A	D	23
?	18	12	30	

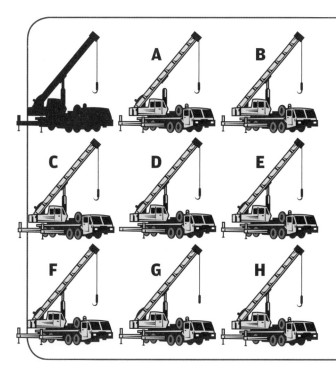

Being Constructive

Which of the coloured-in construction cranes matches the silhouette?

❝When I say artist I mean the man who is building things – creating, moulding the earth – whether it be the plains of the west – or the iron ore of Penn. It's all a big game of construction – some with a brush – some with a shovel, some choose a pen.❞

JACKSON POLLOCK

Apple of the Eye

Can you spot the ten differences between these pictures?

❝Goodness comes out of people who bask in the sun, as it does out of a sweet apple roasted before the fire.❞

CHARLES DUDLEY WARNER

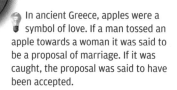

In ancient Greece, apples were a symbol of love. If a man tossed an apple towards a woman it was said to be a proposal of marriage. If it was caught, the proposal was said to have been accepted.

Noughts & Crosses

The numbers around the edge of the grid describe the number of X's in the vertical, horizontal and diagonal lines connecting with that square. Complete the grid so that there is an X or O in every square.

❝Beauty is power; a smile is its sword.❞

JOHN RAY

💡 In humans, type O is the most common blood type.

4	2	3	3	2	0
3					3
4					3
2					2
4					3
0	4	3	4	3	4

Patch of the Day

Place the shape over the grid so that no colour appears twice in the same row or column. Beware, the shape may not be the right way up!

💡 Of the 40 million e-mails generated by his administration, Bill Clinton sent only two whilst he was president – one to test his email address, the second to astronaut John Glenn whilst he was orbiting the earth.

45p

£2.28

42p

£4.85

DIFFICULTY
☆ ★ ★ ✏ ▯

Gone Shopping

You're in a fruit market buying ingredients for a giant fruit salad. You bought 11 pieces of fruit, paid £15.00 and got 25 pence change... What did you buy?

❝If men liked shopping, they'd call it research.❞

CYNTHIA NELMS

> The pineapple was named because of its resemblance to a pinecone by the English in 1664. The native tribes of Central America called it *nana*, meaning "flavour".

DIFFICULTY
☆ ★ ★ ✏ ▯

MARIGOLD   SNAKE

TORTOISE   DAISY

The Secret Garden

The numbers on the side and bottom of the grid indicate occupied squares or groups of consecutive occupied squares in each row or column. Can you finish the grid so that it contains three marigolds, snakes, tortoises and daisies, and the numbers tally?

❝Gardening is the art that uses flowers and plants as paint, and the soil and sky as canvas.❞

ELIZABETH MURRAY

2 1

2 2

1 2

7

3 3

2 3

7

2	7	4	1	6	1	5
2			2		4	
1			1			

💡 In 1978, Princess Margaret became only the second member of the British Royal Family to divorce. The first was Henry VIII in 1533.

Same Difference

By examining the relationships of the following shapes, can you identify the next shape?

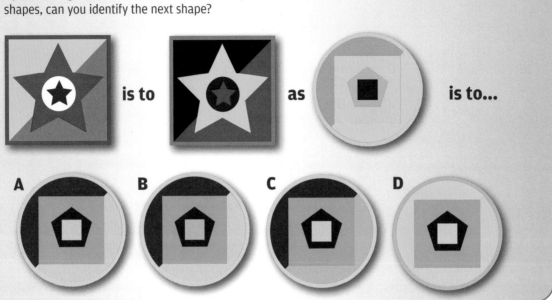

is to   **as**   **is to...**

A   **B**   **C**   **D**

T-Shirt Teaser

This new T-shirt design features the colours red, white and blue in the outlined areas. No area borders another area of the same colour. Can you work out what colour the collar is?

💡 Jimi Hendrix, Janis Joplin and Jim Morrison all died at the age of 27.

Making Sense

The tiles below have been rearranged. Can you work out the new sequence from the clues given below?

The word 'utopia' actually translates from the original Greek as 'no place' or 'the place that does not exist.'

- The two numbers in the middle total 6.
- The number 5 is immediately to the left of the number 6.
- The two left hand numbers total the same as the bottom row.

Knight's Move

Find an empty square in the grid that is one chess knight's move away from a blue, red and yellow circle. A knight's move is an 'L' shape – two squares sideways, up or down in any direction, followed by one square to the left or right.

Although widely thought to be the birthplace of chess, Iran actually banned the game for a little under ten years after the Islamic revolution of 1979. Ayatollah Khomeini said that the game "hurts memory and may cause brain damage."

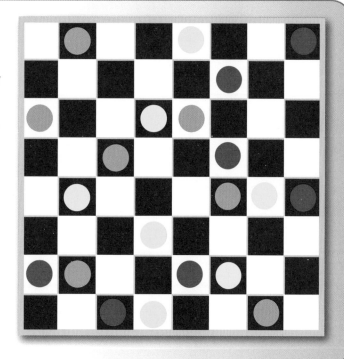

Find the Spies!

A Morse code transmission containing the identity of some of the enemy's top female spies has been intercepted. Unfortunately, spaces between the letters and words are missing. Using the Morse code key below can you find the names of the ten femme fatales?

Morse Code

A .-	B -...	S ...
C -.-.	D -..	T -
E .	F ..-.	U ..-
G --.	H	V ...-
I ..	J .---	W .--
K -.-	L .-..	X -..-
M --	N -.	Y -.--
O ---	P .--.	Z --..
Q --.-	R .-.	

💡 In 1995, the US Coastguard officially stopped using Morse code communications because the majority of vessels were by then fitted with a global maritime distress safety system.

> **And in the end, it's not the years in your life that count. It's the life in your years.**
> ABRAHAM LINCOLN

Police Percentages

Officers Kaplutski and Wojowitz were arguing about how good they both were as cops. It turned out that of the cases they had worked on together, Kaplutski had solved 48 percent, while Wojowitz had solved 52 percent. What is the lowest number of cases they could have worked on?

The 'blood' in the famous shower scene in Alfred Hitchcock's *Psycho* is actually chocolate syrup.

Peculiar Percentages

What percentage of this shape is blue and what percentage is orange?

66 Security is not the meaning of my life. Great opportunities are worth the risks. 99

SHIRLEY HUFSTEDLER

Over 200,000 telephone calls are made daily in the Pentagon through phones connected by 100,000 miles of telephone cable.

Picture Logic Puzzle

The numbers by each row and column describe black squares and groups of black squares that are adjoining. Colour in all the black squares and a six number combination will be revealed.

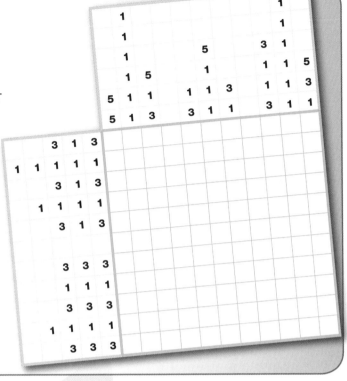

💡 *Don Quixote*, by Miguel de Cervantes Saavedra, has been translated into more languages than any book other than the Bible.

❝Books are divided into two classes: the books of the hour and the books of all time.❞
JOHN RUSKIN

Layered Logic

Can you work out the logic behind the numbers in these shapes, and what A + B totals?

4

24   **A**   **B**

❝No stream rises higher than its source. What ever man might build could never express or reflect more than he was. He could record neither more nor less than he had learned of life when the buildings were built.❞
FRANK LLOYD WRIGHT

💡 In 1978, James Dyson realised the domestic vacuum cleaner needed to be improved. The first generation Dyson arrived five years and 5,127 prototypes later. The company has to date sold over $10 billion of units worldwide.

Hollywood Sign

Can you crack the logical secret behind the numbers next to these star autographs, and discover what number might be next to Tom Cruise?

Johnny Depp 20

WILL SMITH 46

Reese Witherspoon 126

Julia Roberts 50

TOM CRUISE ?

At Mann's Chinese Theatre in Los Angeles, the first foot prints were made by silent movie star Norma Talmadge in 1927, who accidentally stepped in wet concrete outside the venue. Ever since then, more than 180 stars have visited the same spot to leave their hand and foot prints.

On the Radar

The numbers in some cells in the grid indicate the exact number of black cells that should border it. Shade these black, until all the numbers are surrounded by the correct number of black cells.

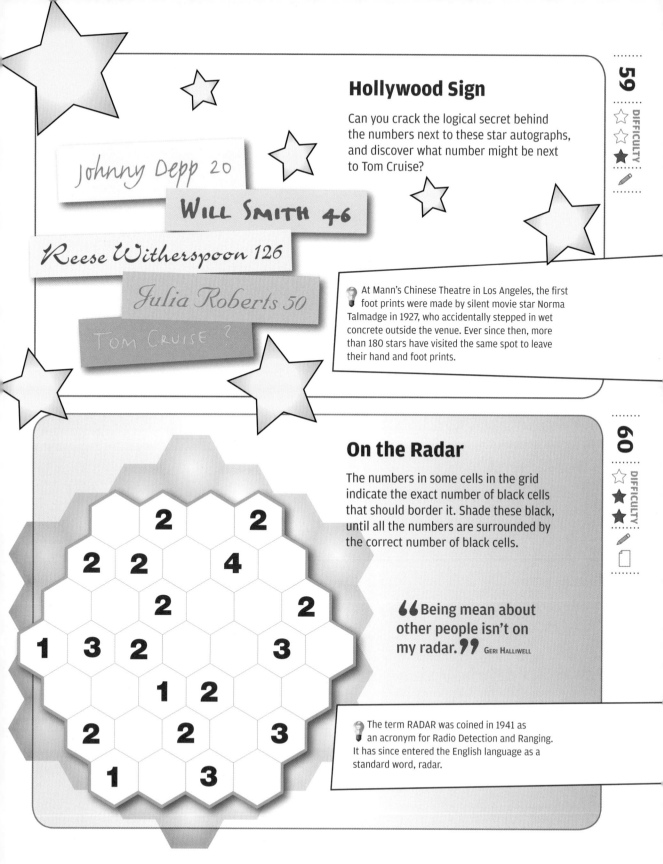

> **❝Being mean about other people isn't on my radar.❞** GERI HALLIWELL

The term RADAR was coined in 1941 as an acronym for Radio Detection and Ranging. It has since entered the English language as a standard word, radar.

DIFFICULTY ★★★ 🖊

61

Cocktail Mixer

Which box has exactly the right pieces to make the cocktail?

❝If you want an interesting party sometime, combine cocktails and a fresh box of crayons for everyone. ❞ ROBERT FULGHUM

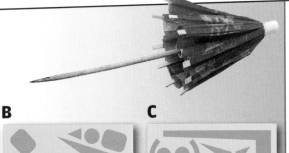

💡 The Sazerac is one of the oldest known cocktails. It is based on a combination of cognac and bitters, and absinthe is used in the preparation of the glass. It was created by Antoine Amédée Peychaud in New Orleans, Louisiana, and given its name by John Schiller in 1859 upon the opening of his Sazerac Coffee House in the same city.

A   **B**   **C**

DIFFICULTY ☆★★ 🖊 📄

62

Patio Percentage

What percentage of this garden is grass and what percentage is stone?

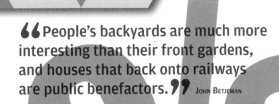

💡 The Greeks invented the system of considering values as part of a hundred, although the term 'percentage' is thought to have been adapted from Italian or French with the % symbol deriving from the Italian abbreviation for 'per cento'.

❝People's backyards are much more interesting than their front gardens, and houses that back onto railways are public benefactors. ❞ JOHN BETJEMAN

Dice Puzzler

What's the missing number?

3   4   10   ?

💡 Brunei and the United Arab Emirates are the only two countries where there is no right to vote.

Card Shuffle

Fill up the shuffle box so that each row, column and long diagonal contains a Jack, Queen, King and Ace of each suit.

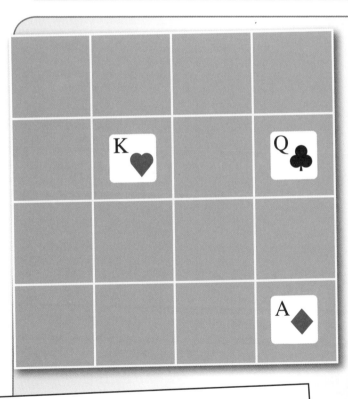

💡 There are over 1,000 variations of the perennially popular game solitaire, all deriving from around a dozen 'base' games.

Shooting Stars

Divide up the grid into four equally sized, equally shaped parts, each containing four different coloured stars.

David Wolf was the first person to cast an absentee ballot from space. In November 1997, he cast a vote via e-mail for the mayor of Houston while onboard the space station *Mir*.

❝If you shoot for the stars and hit the moon, it's OK. But you've got to shoot for something. A lot of people don't even shoot.❞ CONFUCIUS

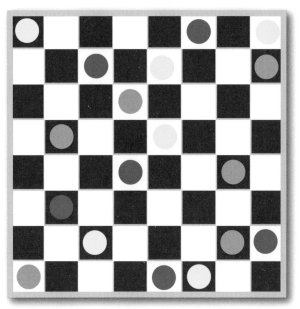

Knight's Move

Find an empty square in the grid that is one chess knight's move away from a blue, red and yellow circle. A knight's move is an 'L' shape – two squares sideways, up or down in any direction, followed by one square to the left or right.

💡 Avalon is a mythical island located somewhere in Great Britain. Mentioned in Arthurian legend it was, as early as the 12th century, linked to Glastonbury Tor in Somerset, where the bones of King Arthur and his queen were supposedly uncovered. It remains associated with present-day Glastonbury.

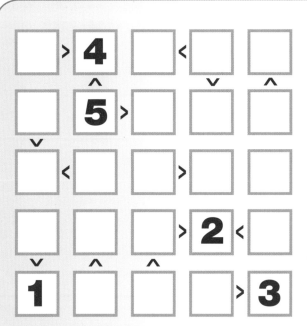

Tough Going

The arrows indicate whether a number in a box is greater or smaller than an adjacent number. Complete the grid so that all rows and columns contain the numbers 1 to 5.

❝ The story is more important to me than the part. ❞
CATHERINE DENEUVE

💡 Frederick the Great of Prussia tried to ban the consumption of coffee and demanded that the populace drink alcohol instead.

Around the Block

DIFFICULTY ☆ ★ ★

Can you crack the colour code and make your way from one yellow square to the other, moving one square at a time? The blue arrow tells you which way is up...

66 Happiness is not being pained in body or troubled in mind. 99 THOMAS JEFFERSON

UP

 The Atlantic giant squid has larger eyes than any other animal, either alive or extinct. One specimen had eyes with an estimated diameter of 50 centimetres.

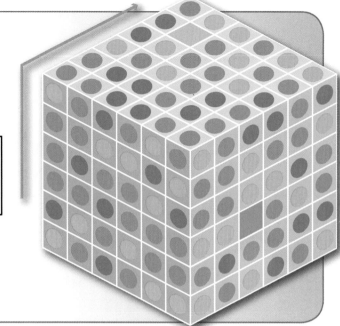

DIFFICULTY ☆ ★ ★

Priceless Pottery

The areas outlined on this vase will be painted blue, red and green, and no two areas that touch each other can be the same colour. What colour should the handle be?

66 You can only mend the vase so many times before you have to chuck it away. 99

CHRISTINE McVIE

 Josiah Wedgwood, one of the most innovative figures in the history of pottery, was elected a fellow of the Royal Society in 1783, primarily for inventing the pyrometer to measure oven temperatures. He had been the appointed 'Queen's Potter' since 1762.

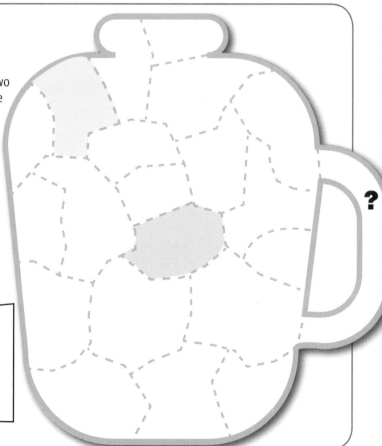

Lost Swatch

One of our swatches is missing! Can you work out the four colour sequence that completes the set?

66 The purest and most thoughtful minds are those which love colour the most. 99

JOHN RUSKIN

Find the Treasure

The numbers on the side and bottom of the grid indicate occupied squares or groups of consecutive occupied squares in each row or column. Can you finish the grid so that it contains two Amulets, two Cutlasses, three bars of Gold and two Keys, and the numbers tally?

💡 It was Plutarch, the Greek historian, who gave the first definition of piracy as an illegal attack on a ship or coastal city.

66 The average man will bristle if you say his father was dishonest, but he will brag a little if he discovers that his great-grandfather was a pirate. 99

BERN WILLIAMS

AMULET **CUTLASS**

GOLD

GOLD **KEY**

2 2
3 1
2 1
2 1
1 1
1 2
5

2 7 2 1 2 2 1
1 1 2 2 1

Making Shapes

Which of the pictures below represents the correct overhead view of this scene?

❝A cynic is a man who knows the price of everything but the value of nothing.❞ OSCAR WILDE

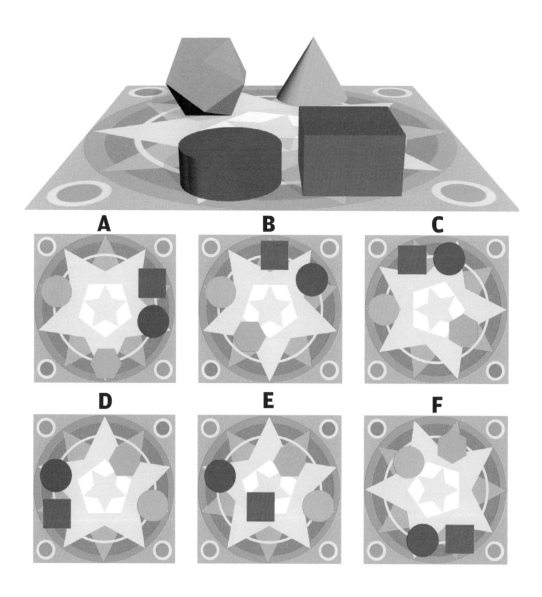

💡 The botanical gardens in the Argentine capital Buenos Aires were designed in 1898 by the French landscaper Carlos Thays, and occupy 69,722 m² of the city's northern district of Palermo. Today they are best known for the huge number of feral cats that call the garden home.

Amounting to Something

Use the white numbers to make the central number the same way in all three cases. What number should replace the question mark?

💡 F. Scott Fitzgerald was named after a distant relative, Francis Scott Key, who wrote the words to the *Star Spangled Banner* in 1814.

In a Spin

What numbers should appear in the hubs of these number tornadoes?

66 A man of genius has been seldom ruined but by himself. 99
SAMUEL JOHNSON

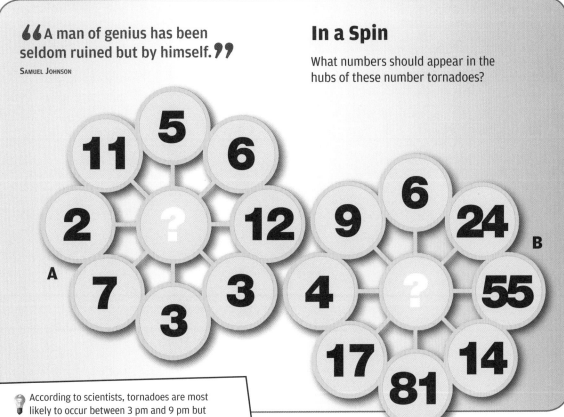

💡 According to scientists, tornadoes are most likely to occur between 3 pm and 9 pm but can occur at any time.

Reach the Top

Replace the question marks with numbers so that each pair of blocks adds up to the block directly above them.

❝I'll love you, dear, I'll love you till China and Africa meet and the river jumps over the mountain and the salmon sing in the street.❞ W. H. Auden

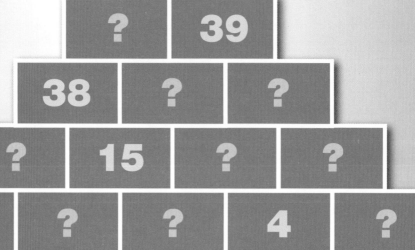

Minesweeper

The numbered squares in the grid indicate the exact number of shaded squares that should surround them. The puzzle is solved when all these squares are surrounded by the correct number of shaded squares.

 Near the confessionals in the Cattedrale di San Lorenzo in Genoa, Italy, lies an unexploded World War II bomb.

1	2			2	2	
3					3	4
			4	2	4		3
4		5	3		4	
				2	3		3
	2	3	2	3		4
2				3		
1		2			2	3

Exactly the Same

Only two of the shapes below are exactly the same; can you find the matching pair?

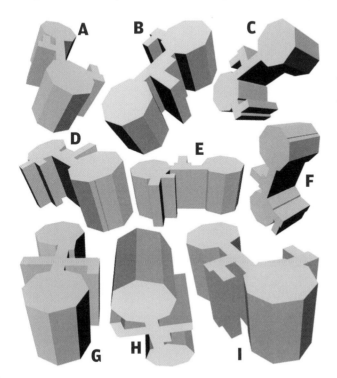

> **There are two things in life for which we are never truly prepared: twins.**
> JOSH BILLINGS

It is believed that the alcoholic drink gin originated in the Netherlands during the 17th century and that it was the invention of Dr Slyvuis, a Professor of Medicine who used it to treat kidney ailments. He called it 'genever' after the French 'genièvre' or 'juniper'.

City Scrape

Luke is considering buying a loft apartment but is concerned that it does not receive enough natural light. Can you work out the approximate area that this cityscape is occupying?

> **A great city is not to be confounded with a populous one.**
> ARISTOTLE

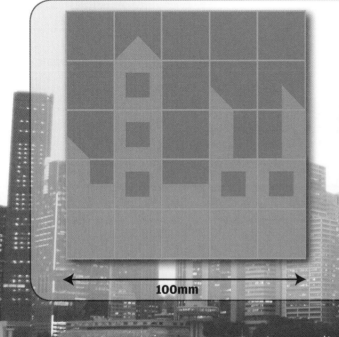

100mm

One of the most famous cityscape paintings is Johannes Vermeer's *View of Delft*, which he composed between 1659 and 1660. It currently hangs in the Mauritshuis in the Hague.

Arrow Escape

Complete the grid by drawing an arrow in each box that points in any one of the eight compass directions (N, E, S, W, NE, NW, SE, SW). The numbers in the outside boxes in the finished puzzle will reflect the number of arrows pointing in their direction.

❝Learning is finding out what you already know. Doing is demonstrating that you know it.❞ RICHARD BACH

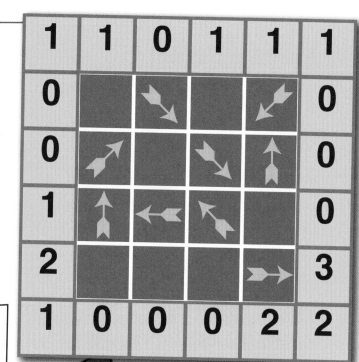

💡 The compass plant was given its name because during midsummer its leaves point precisely north and south.

Acting Parts

These ten pieces can be assembled to spell the name of a movie star . . . Who?

💡 In 2001, the American Film Institute released a list of the 'Most Thrilling Movies in American Cinema'. In reverse order the top three were *The Exorcist* (1973), *Jaws* (1975) and *Psycho* (1960).

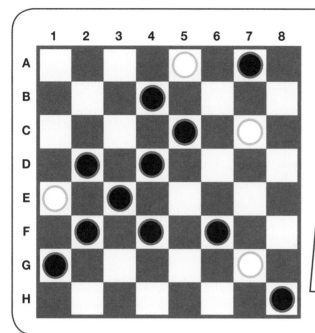

Check This Out

Make a move for white so that eight black pieces are left, none of which are in the same column or row.

❝If life doesn't offer a game worth playing, then invent a new one.❞

ANTHONY J. D'ANGELO

💡 It would take a person typing 60 words per minute, eight hours a day, around 50 years to type the human genome.

Place the Shapes

Place the two shapes over the grid so that no colour appears twice in the same row or column. Beware, the shapes may not be the right way up!

❝Think in the morning. Act in the noon. Eat in the evening. Sleep in the night.❞

WILLIAM BLAKE

💡 Only one national flag is a solid colour: the green flag of Libya.

Make It Up

Divide up the grid into four equally sized, equally shaped parts, each containing numbers that add up to 36.

❝If a man's wit be wandering, let him study the mathematics.❞

FRANCIS BACON

			1	1	1	1		
	4	2	2	2	2	6		
1	2	3	3	3	3	2	2	
2	3	4	7	4	4	3	1	
3	4	0	3	9	5	4	2	
2	1	0	4	1	3	1	2	
	1	7	7	1	4	1		
		1	8	2	0			

💡 Did you know that... 111,111,111 x 111,111,111 = 12,345,678,987,654,321?

Gramo-Phonies

Which box has exactly the right parts to build the gramophone?

A

B

C

💡 On 8 November 1887, German immigrant Emile Berliner patented the gramophone in Washington D.C. having pioneered the technique of sound recording on flat discs or records rather than on cylinders.

Follow That Cab!

The jewel thieves have left their loot in a yellow cab in New York City. They have left directions on how to find the cab in the black car. Can you track down the cab and rescue the rocks?

"The great thieves lead away the little thief." DIOGENES

	1	2	3	4	5	6
A						
B						
C						
D						
E						

2e, 4s, 2w, 1n, 1w,

1s, 4n, 1s, 1w, 4e,

1w, 3s, 2e, 5w, 4n,

3s, 1n, 5e, 4w, 1e,

1n, 3e, 2s, 3n, 2w,

2s, 1s, 1e, 1n

In June, 1926, Spanish architect Antoni Gaudí was run over by a tram in Barcelona. Poorly dressed, he was not recognized and taxi drivers refused to take a 'vagabond' to the hospital (they were later fined by the police). His greatest work, the Sagrada Familia, on which he had been working for nearly 30 years, remains unfinished and he is buried in its crypt.

Dice Puzzle

What's the missing number?

💡 Elvis Presley was a black belt in karate. He took up martial arts under the shotokan sensei Jürgen Seydal, while fulfilling his military duties in Germany in 1958.

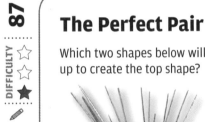

1   9   8   ?

The Perfect Pair

Which two shapes below will pair up to create the top shape?

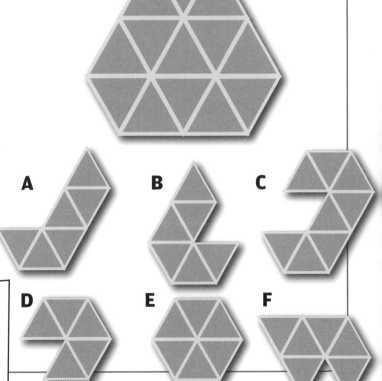

A   B   C

D   E   F

💡 Born Jumping Badger and given the nickname Hunkesni or "slow" as a child due to his methodical nature, the Native American warrior is best known as "Sitting Bull" or Tatanka-Iyotanka.

> **66** An ounce of performance is worth pounds of promises. **99**
> Mae West

Table Topper

Below is a table, ready for mosaic tiles. Can you arrange the groups of tiles to finish it?

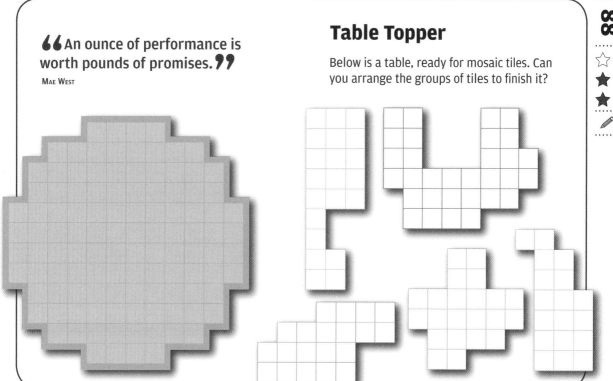

Cube Route

Can you crack the colour code and make your way from one purple square to the other? The blue arrow tells you which way is up . . .

> **66** The mind can make a heaven out of hell or a hell out of heaven. **99** John Milton

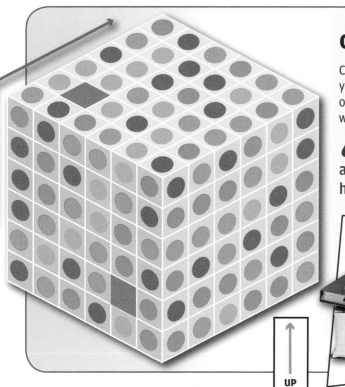

UP

💡 John Milton was blinded by glaucoma in middle age and he composed his epic works *Paradise Lost* (1667) and *Paradise Regained* (1671) through dictation. It is believed that fellow poet Andrew Marvell was one of those who wrote down Milton's words.

A Different View

Of the plan views below, only one of them is a true overhead representation of the scene shown here; can you make out which?

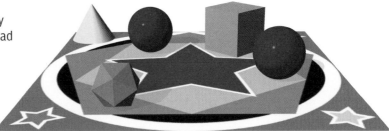

In 1873, the Mauch Chunk Switchback Railway in the Pennsylvania mountains began to carry passengers rather than coal. It is considered to be the first American roller coaster, though some believe LaMarcus Thompson's Switchback roller coaster which opened at Coney Island in 1874 to be the first.

A

B

C

D

E

F

Hard Cell

The numbers in some cells in the grid indicate the exact number of black cells that should border it. Shade these black, until all the numbers are surrounded by the correct number of black cells.

The first known contraceptive was crocodile dung. It was used by the Ancient Egyptians in 2000 BC.

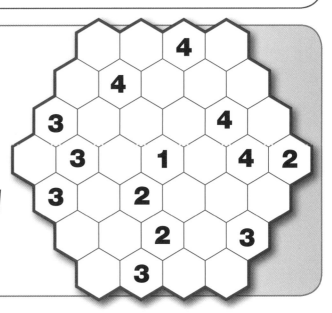

green heads

ducks

black feet

A

B C D

E F G H I

J K L

M

orange beaks

Duck Hunt

Can you work out which areas of this diagram represent ducks with orange beaks that don't have black feet or green heads, and green-headed, black-footed birds that aren't ducks and don't have orange beaks?

❝If it looks like a duck, and quacks like a duck, we have at least to consider the possibility that we have a small aquatic bird of the family anatidae on our hands.❞ DOUGLAS ADAMS

💡 All of the Peking ducks in the United States are direct descendants of nine ducks imported to Long Island in 1873.

Make the Shape

Which two shapes below will pair up to create the top shape?

❝All of us are guinea pigs in the laboratory of God. Humanity is just a work in progress.❞

TENNESSEE WILLIAMS

💡 In 1895, the Swedish chemist Svante Arrhenius discovered that humans could enhance the greenhouse effect by making carbon dioxide, a greenhouse gas.

A   **B**   **C**

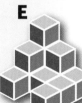   

D   **E**   **F**

Ball Logic

The balls below have been rearranged. Can you work out the new sequence of the balls from the clues given below?

• The 2 ball isn't touching the 5 or the 4.
• The 4 ball is touching the 10 but not the 6.
• The 8 ball is immediately to the left of the 6.
• The bottom row totals 16.

❝It's good sportsmanship not to pick up lost balls while they are still rolling.❞ MARK TWAIN

Chess Move

Can you place a queen, a bishop, a knight and a rook on this chessboard so that the blue squares are attacked by exactly two pieces, the green ones by three pieces and the red ones by four pieces?

Double Drat

All these shapes appear twice in the box except one. Can you spot it?

> **Anybody can be pope; the proof of this is that I have become one.**
> POPE JOHN XXIII

💡 In 1624, Pope Urban VIII threatened to excommunicate snuff tobacco users.

Fisherman's Riddle

Jose the Fisherman passed away, leaving his fleet of 17 fishing boats to his three daughters. He stipulated in his will that his eldest daughter, Manuela, should get half the boats, his second daughter, Maria, should get one-third of them, and his youngest, Monica, should get one-ninth of the fleet. The girls were at a loss as to how they were supposed to carry out their father's last wish, until another fisherman offered to help them . . . What did he do?

> **The fishermen know that the sea is dangerous and the storm terrible, but they have never found these dangers sufficient reason for remaining ashore.** VINCENT VAN GOGH

Island Spy

The four squares below can all be found in the picture grid; can you track them down? Beware, they may not be the right way up!

66 **True friendship multiplies the good in life and divides its evils. Strive to have friends, for life without friends is like life on a desert island... to find one real friend in a lifetime is good fortune; to keep him is a blessing.** 99 BALTASAR GRACIAN

💡 Of the 6 billion plus people in the world, one in ten lives on an island (600 million). Some 60 million live in Britain, the only island connected to a continent (through the Channel Tunnel).

Mystery Symmetry

This picture, when finished, is symmetrical along a vertical line up the middle. Can you colour in the missing squares and work out what the picture is of?

66 **We build statues out of snow, and weep to see them melt.** 99 SIR WALTER SCOTT

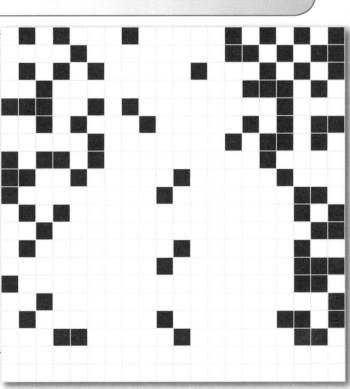

💡 The Inuit language has more than 20 words for snow and Inuit women have a tradition of never combing their hair on the day a polar bear is to be killed.

3	4	3	2	3	1
3			O		3
4		O		O	2
5					5
3	O		O		3
1	5	3	4	4	3

Noughts & Crosses

The numbers around the edge of the grid describe the number of Xs in the vertical, horizontal and diagonal lines connecting with that square. Complete the grid so that there is an X or O in every square.

66 Who in the world am I? Ah, that's the great puzzle. 99
LEWIS CARROLL

The head of a woodpecker striking a tree is travelling at more than 1,300 miles per hour - twice the speed of a bullet.

Matching Motor Cars

A

B

C

D

E

F

G

H

I

Only two of these cars are exactly the same; can you find the matching pair?

66 A suburban mother's role is to deliver children obstetrically once, and by car for ever after. 99 PETER DE VRIES

The Indianapolis Speedway Stadium built in 1909 can claim to be the biggest in the world. It has a capacity of 250,000 in its all-seater complex.

DIFFICULTY ☆ ★ ★

Corkscrew Caper

Which of the coloured-in corkscrews matches the silhouette?

❝What though youth gave love and roses, Age still leaves us friends and wine.❞

THOMAS MORE

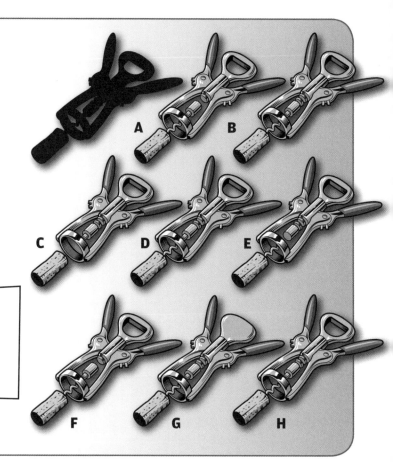

💡 There are approximately 3,000 wineries in the United States – 1,300 of these are in California. The state is the fourth ranked wine producer by volume in the world, after Italy, France and Spain.

DIFFICULTY ☆ ★ ★

Tents and Trees

Every tree has one tent found horizontally or vertically adjacent to it. No tent can be in an adjacent square to another tent (even diagonally). The numbers by each row and column tell you how many tents are there. Can you locate all the tents?

TREE   **TENT**

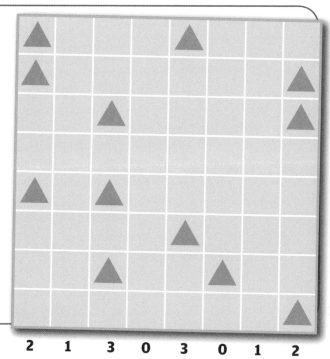

💡 One of the very first official camping sites in the UK was Cunningham Camp in Howstrake, Isle of Man. It opened in 1894; and strangely enough all of the campers were male.

Spare Part

All these pictures below show constructions built from three of the spare part. Except one! Can you find the different design?

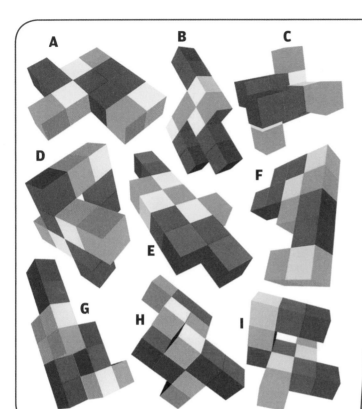

SPARE PART

💡 In 1869, Russian chemist Dimitry Ivanovich Mendeleyev developed the Periodic Table of the Elements – a chart that reflected their properties and that went on to become a common sight in chemistry classrooms the world over.

Paint Planning

This wall is to be painted in green, blue and lilac, with no adjacent bricks to be in the same colour. Can you work out what colour the window frame should be?

?

A Piece of Pie

Can you crack the pie code and fill in the missing numbers?

❝If you want to make an apple pie from scratch, you must first create the universe. ❞ Dr. Carl Sagan

💡 Brasília, the modern capital of Brazil, was officially opened on 22 April 1960. It was a federal decision to build a new rigidly planned city away from the country's sea border so it would be less susceptible to sea invasion.

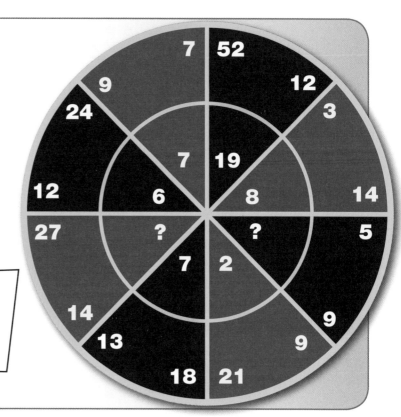

Five Point Problem

The numbers on these pentagons follow a pattern. Your task is to uncover the secret to the pattern and fill in the blanks to complete the puzzle.

Beethoven 40

Mozart 16

Schubert 24

Bach 6

Vivaldi ?

Composer Poser

Can you crack the logical secret behind the numbers by these famous composers, and work out what number Vivaldi might be?

❝I pay no attention whatever to anybody's praise or blame. I simply follow my own feelings. ❞ WOLFGANG AMADEUS MOZART

💡 In 1762, the two prodigiously talented Mozart children, which included Wolfgang Amadeus aged just six, embarked on the first of a series of concert tours across Europe.

❝Too many have dispensed with generosity in order to practise charity. ❞ ALBERT CAMUS

Shaping Relations

By examining the relationships of the following shapes, can you identify the next shape?

is to ... **as** ... **is to...**

A   **B**   **C**   **D**

Camel Capers

Can you work out the approximate area the image of the camel is occupying?

66 There is no logical reason why the camel of great art should pass through the needle of mob intelligence. **99** REBECCA WEST

💡 Llamas are very closely related to camels. In fact a camel-llama crossbreed was born in Dubai in 1997. It was called Rama the cama.

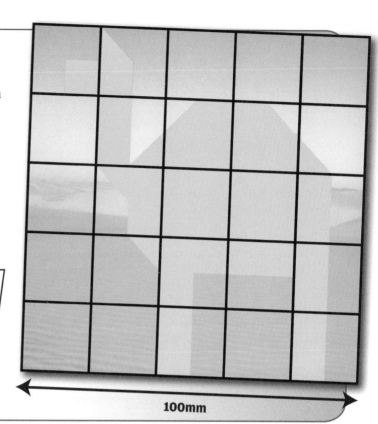

100mm

Star Detective

The stars shown below have been rearranged. Can you work out the new sequence from the clues given below?

• The red shapes are adjacent, the yellows are not.
• The top shape is a red circle.
• On the bottom, a square is to the right of a blue shape.

💡 The famous American National Spelling Bee was launched by the *Courier-Journal* of Louisville, Kentucky, in 1925 as an attempt to raise childrens' interest in the subject.

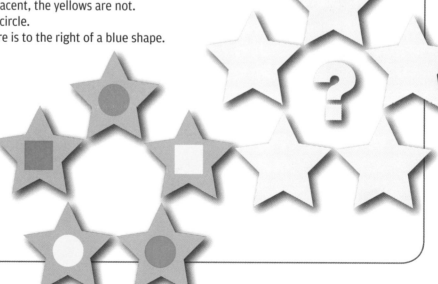

Size Matters

Can you put these shapes in order, from biggest to smallest?

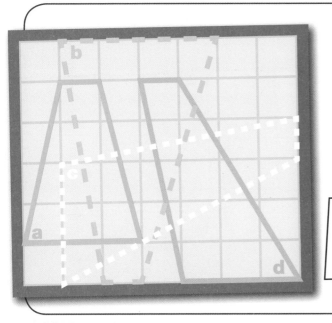

❝ What counts is not necessarily the size of the dog in the fight; it's the size of the fight in the dog. ❞

DWIGHT DAVID EISENHOWER

💡 The missionary Hans Egede founded Nuuk in 1728 as the very first town in Greenland. It is now the country's capital with a permanent population of only 15,000.

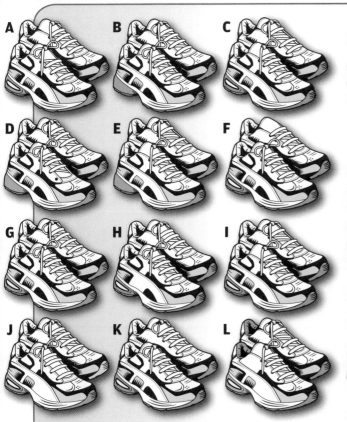

Sneaky Sneakers

Only two of these pairs of trainers are exactly the same. Can you spot the matching pair?

❝ My verses, I cannot say poems. I was following in the exquisite footsteps of Miss Millay, unhappily in my own horrible sneakers. ❞ DOROTHY PARKER

💡 Every year since 1985 Nike have released a new Air Jordan basketball shoe. The Air Jordan II was the first regular sneaker to have a triple digit price tag in the United States.

Building Block

Which two shapes below can be combined to create the top shape?

66 The absolute yearning of one human body for another particular body and its indifference to substitutes is one of life's major mysteries. **99**

IRIS MURDOCH

💡 The human head contains 22 bones, consisting of the cranium and the facial bones. The cranium is formed by eight bones and the face consists of 14 bones including the maxilla (upper jaw) and mandible (lower jaw).

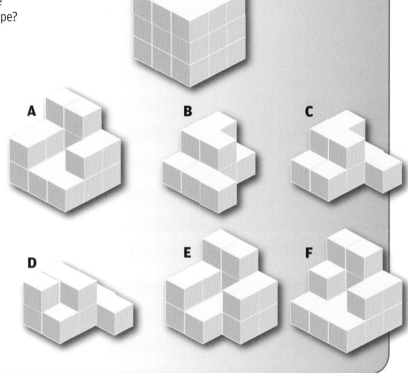

Number Wheel

What numbers should appear in the hubs of these number wheels?

💡 The tomato is the world's most popular fruit. More than 60 million tons of tomatoes are produced per year, 16 million tons more than the second most popular fruit, the banana. Apples are the third most popular (36 million tons), then oranges (34 million tons) and watermelons (22 million tons).

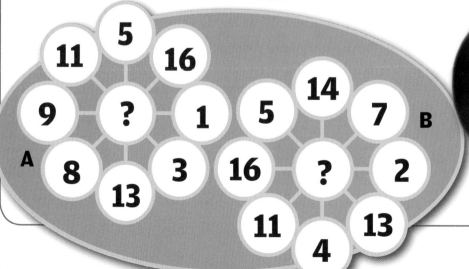

Mystery Middle

The columns and rows that make up the finished grid have certain properties in common. Identify these matching qualities and you should be able to work out which of the squares below will correctly complete the grid.

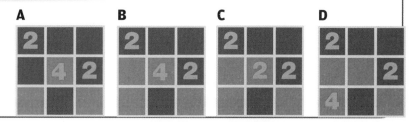

A **B** **C** **D**

💡 The last battle to be held on mainland British soil was the 1746 Battle of Culloden Moor, where British forces defeated the rebel Scots, who were led by the exiled 'Bonnie' Prince Charlie.

A Colourful Path

Find a path from one white cell to the other in the shortest way. You may only pass from a red cell to a blue one, a blue to a yellow, a yellow to a green or a green to a red.

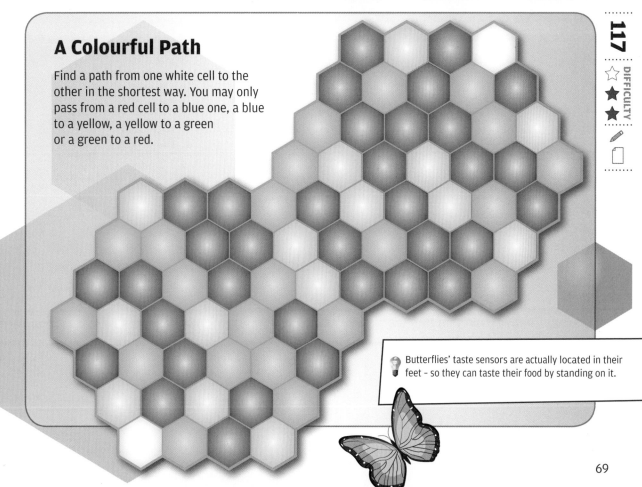

💡 Butterflies' taste sensors are actually located in their feet – so they can taste their food by standing on it.

Get the Picture

These two grids, when merged together, will make a picture... Of what?

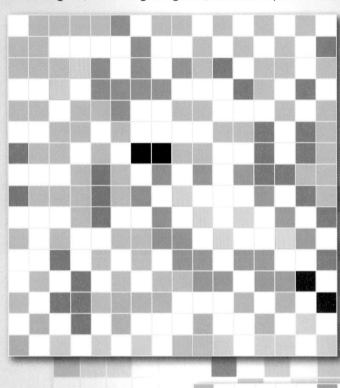

> **Every artist dips his brush in his own soul, and paints his own nature into his pictures.** HENRY WARD BEECHER

Elmyr de Hory was a famous Hungarian-born art forger. His claim to have sold over 1,000 forgeries to galleries worldwide made him the subject of an Orson Welles documentary *F for Fake*. Ironically his celluloid exposure actually created a market for his forged works.

Odd One Out

Study the shapes on the left; which of the shapes below is not the same as the other ones?

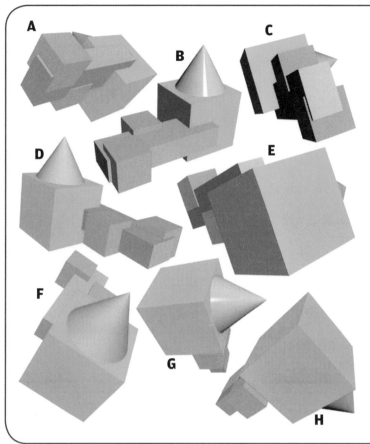

66 Logic: The art of thinking and reasoning in strict accordance with the limitations and incapacities of the human misunderstanding. **99**

AMBROSE BIERCE

Dicey Directions

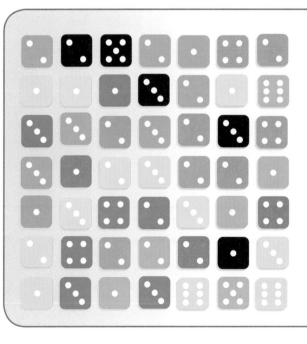

Each colour represents a different direction. Starting in the middle die of the grid, follow the instructions correctly and you will visit every die in turn once only. What's the last die you visit on your trip?

Pink = Left
Red = Right
Black = Down
Yellow = Up
Purple = Up Right
Brown = Down Right
Blue = Up Left
Green = Down Left

💡 The most famous hedge maze in the world is situated at Hampton Court Palace near London. It was planted in 1702 and covers approximately 1,350 square metres.

Dotty Dilemma

Complete the grid so that all rows and columns contain the numbers 1, 2, 3, 4, 5 and 6. Areas with a dotted outline contain numbers that add up to the total shown.

❝Do not anticipate trouble or worry about what may never happen. Keep in the sunlight.❞
BENJAMIN FRANKLIN

💡 It is thought that plant-eating dinosaurs did not eat grass, because there wasn't any. During the Mesozoic Era, when the dinosaurs lived, conifers - cone-bearing trees and shrubs – dominated the landscape.

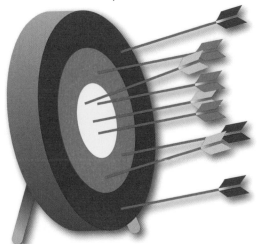

Think Back

Study these images for a minute, cover them up and then answer the five questions below.

Questions:
1. How many pink-flighted arrows were there altogether? 2. Which colour arrows scored most bullseyes?
3. How many blue arrows landed in the red sections? 4. How many green arrows landed in the blue sections?
5. What colour was the arrow highest up on the first target?

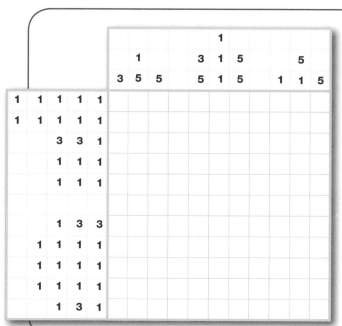

All Will Be Revealed

The numbers by each row and column describe black squares and groups of black squares that are adjoining. Colour in all the black squares and a six number combination will be revealed.

💡 More than 5 billion crayons are produced each year and it is estimated that more than 100 billion crayons have been produced so far.

DIFFICULTY ☆ ★ ★ ✏️

Scales

The arms of these scales are divided into sections – a weight two sections away from the middle will be twice as heavy as a weight one section away. Can you arrange the supplied weights in order to balance the whole scale?

DIFFICULTY ★ ★ ★ ✏️ 📄

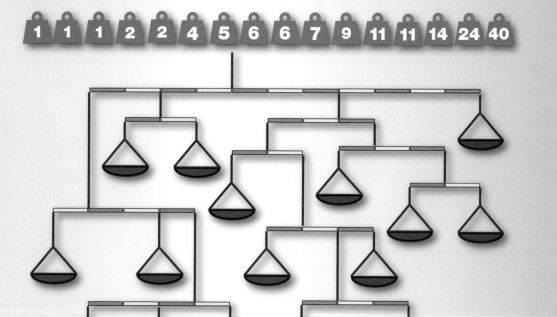

73

Bits and Pieces

These ten pieces can be arranged to spell out the name of a famous historical figure... but who?

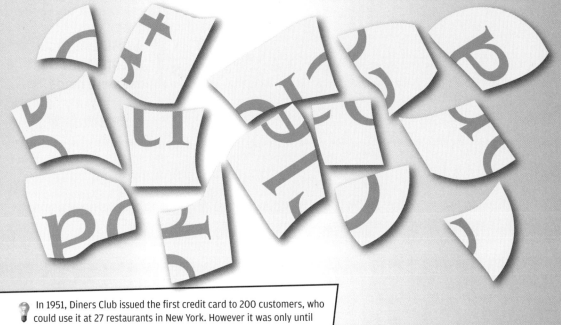

In 1951, Diners Club issued the first credit card to 200 customers, who could use it at 27 restaurants in New York. However it was only until the establishment of standards for the magnetic strip in 1970 that the credit card became part of the information age.

Next in Line

The sequence below follows a logical pattern. Can you work out the number and colour next in line?

1 2 1 2 1 1 1 ?

Roy Orbison's signature sunglasses look had an innocent explanation. Early in his career he accidentally left his regular glasses in an airplane. Unable to wear contact lenses, the only others he had were a pair of prescription sunglasses which he wore to perform and went on to become his trademark.

Shady Squares

The numbers in some squares in the grid indicate the exact number of shaded squares that should surround it. Colour in the squares until all the numbers are surrounded by the correct number of shaded squares, and a number will be revealed!

	5		5		5		3		4		5		3	1
5		6		7		6		5		6		6		3
	4		6		7		6		6		5		7	
2		3		7		6		7		5		6		4
	1		6		4		5		7		6		7	
0		4		6		3		7		6		7		4
	3		8		3		5		6		5		8	
1		6		4		3		8		5		6		5
	4		6		1		3		6		6		6	
2		5		2		1		4		5		4		2

> **"Hide not your talents. They for use were made. What's a sundial in the shade?"**
> BENJAMIN FRANKLIN

> 💡 More than 2,700 different languages are spoken in the world, with more than 7,000 dialects. Mandarin is the most spoken language in the world, followed by English. However, as a home language, Spanish is the second most spoken in the world.

Numbers Up

The arrows indicate whether a number in a box is greater or smaller than an adjacent number. Complete the grid so that all rows and columns contain the numbers 1 to 5.

> **"Liberty means responsibility. That is why most men dread it."**
> GEORGE BERNARD SHAW

> 💡 On Wednesday, 17 June 1885, the Statue of Liberty arrived in New York Harbour aboard the French ship *Isere*.

Power Boats

The power boat race follows the course below. Can you work out the last buoy the boat must reach to finish?

2N, 3E, 2S, 2S, 3N, 1E, 3S, 1N, 5W, 1S, 2N, 5E, 2N, 5W, 2E, 1E, 4S, 2W, 1E, 3N, 2W, 3E, 2W, 2S, 3E, 1W, 1W, 1N, 1E.

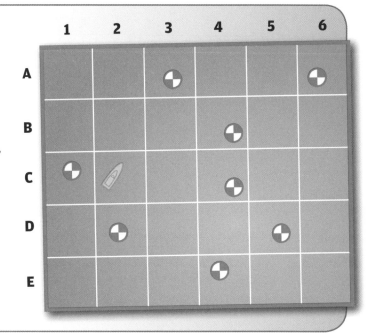

❝A ship is safe in harbour, but that's not what ships are for.❞
WILLIAM SHEDD

Strange Shapes

Only two of the shapes below are exactly the same. Can you find the matching pair?

❝I am not afraid of death, I just don't want to be there when it happens.❞ WOODY ALLEN

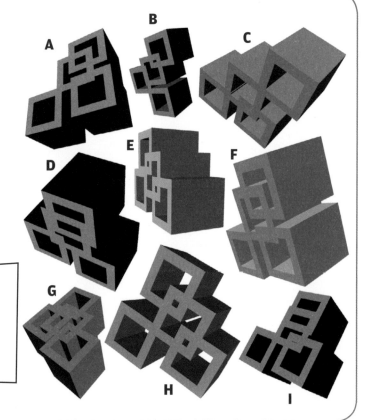

💡 In 1974, Australia's Northern Territory was devastated by Cyclone Tracy. The eye of the storm was only 12 km in diameter over Darwin - extremely small for a cyclone - yet 70% of the city's residential buildings suffered structural damage.

Seeing Stars

Can you find three perfect five-pointed stars in this colourful collection?

66 **Dreams permit each and every one of us to be quietly and safely insane every night of our lives.** 99 WILLIAM DEMENT

💡 The first recorded use of fireworks in England was at the wedding celebrations of Henry VII in 1476. Queen Elizabeth created the post of Fireworks Master, making sure someone was in charge of displays to mark grand state occasions.

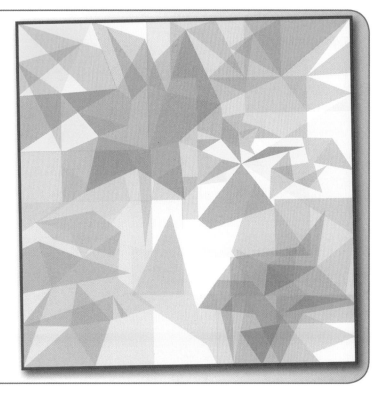

Take a Tip

Three men share a taxi ride and the bill comes to £25. They each hand the taxi driver £10 and he puts it in his cash box. The taxi driver owes them £5 change, but gives them each £1 and slips the other £2 into his pocket as a tip. The men have paid £9 each, making £27. The driver has £2 in his pocket, that makes £29. Where is the other pound?

66 **Never throughout history has a man who lived a life of ease left a name worth remembering.** 99

THEODORE ROOSEVELT

DIFFICULTY ☆ ★ ★ ✎

Plane Poser

Which box has exactly the right parts to complete the model airplane?

A

B

C

💡 Henri Fabre's floatplane was the first aircraft to take off from water in Martigues, France, in March 1910.

❝A man may die, nations may rise and fall, but an idea lives on.❞ JOHN F. KENNEDY

DIFFICULTY ★ ★ ★ ✎ ▢

Box Values

The value of each shape is the number of sides each shape has, multiplied by the number within it. So a square containing the number 4 has a value of 16. Find a block of four squares (two squares wide by two squares high) with a total value of exactly 60.

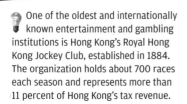

💡 One of the oldest and internationally known entertainment and gambling institutions is Hong Kong's Royal Hong Kong Jockey Club, established in 1884. The organization holds about 700 races each season and represents more than 11 percent of Hong Kong's tax revenue.

Spell it Out

Arrange these ten pieces to spell out the name of a famous composer.

Where's the Pair?

Only two of these pictures are exactly the same. Can you find the matching pair?

> 66 Bad times have a scientific value. These are occasions a good learner would not miss. 99
>
> RALPH WALDO EMERSON

💡 In 1905, Hans Wildorf, a German living in London, established a firm that dealt in watches with his English brother-in-law. Originally called Wildorf & Davies, it is now much better known by the brand name Rolex, which he chose in 1908.

Get out of This!

You're playing stripes in a game of pool, and you've cleaned up all your balls.
You're snookered on the black though... Can you spot the shot?

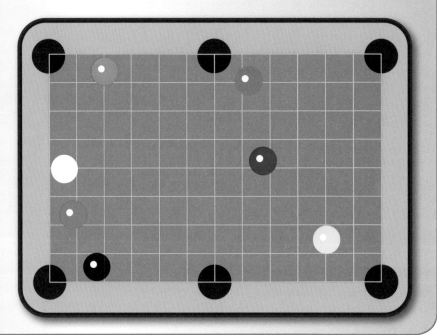

💡 During a billiards title match held on 1 September 1865 in Detroit, Michighan, a fly landed on the ball that Louis Fox was aiming at. The distraction snapped Fox's concentration and he missed the shot; his opponent then ran the table and won the match. Two days later, Fox's body was discovered floating in a river where he'd apparently drowned himself.

Fold and Cut

Which of the doily patterns below is created by this fold and cut?

66 All I need is my brains, my eyes and my personality, for better or for worse. **99**

WILLIAM ALBERT ALLARD

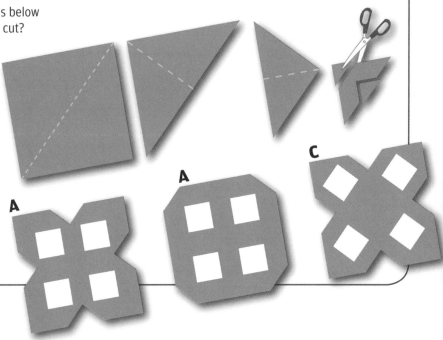

A

A

C

💡 On average, women blink nearly twice as much as men.

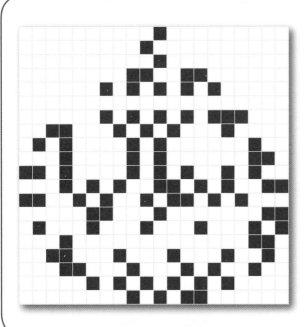

Missing Squares

This picture, when finished, is symmetrical along a vertical line up the middle. Can you colour in the missing squares and work out what the picture is of?

❝I believe humans get a lot done, not because we're smart, but because we have thumbs so we can make coffee.❞ FLASH ROSENBERG

💡 Coffee giant Starbucks takes its name from the character of the first mate in Herman Melville's *Moby Dick*.

Piecing It Together

Which three of the pieces below can complete the jigsaw and make a perfect square?

❝Sloth makes all things difficult, but industry, all things easy. He that rises late must trot all day, and shall scarce overtake his business at night, while laziness travels so slowly that poverty soon overtakes him.❞ BENJAMIN FRANKLIN

A B C D E F

Alien Identification

Ziplock from the planet Velkro isn't green and doesn't have feelers on his head. He does have a tail though, and an odd number of eyes... Can you pick him out?

❝For me every ruler is alien that defies public opinion. ❞

MOHANDAS GANDHI

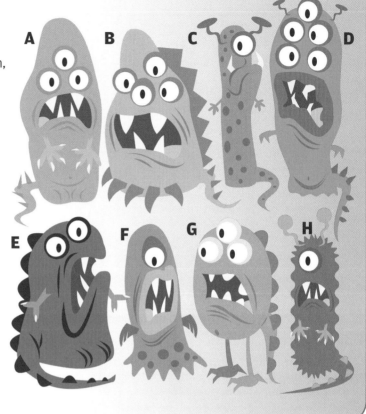

💡 The Tuatara, a rare lizard-like reptile native to New Zealand, has three eyes. The third, called a parietal eye, is well-developed but is only visible in hatchlings. After time it is obscured by scales and pigmentation.

Carrot Casino

Two rabbits were trying to sort out their complicated carrot debts and IOUs following a game of rabbit poker.

Thumper gave Cottontail as many carrots as Cottontail had. Then Cottontail gave Thumper back as much as Thumper had left. Thumper then gave Cottontail as much as Cottontail had left. At the end, Thumper had no carrots and Cottontail had 80. How many did they each start with?

💡 The longest continuous war was the 'Thirty Years War', fought between various European countries from 1618 to 1648.

View from Above

Of the plan views below, only one of them is a true overhead representation of the scene shown here; can you work out which?

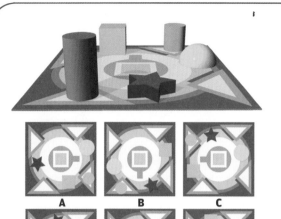

A **B** **C**

D **E** **F**

66 Not everybody is perfect, and I don't think we should be looking for perfect people. 99

SIMON COWELL

💡 It is a common mistake to say that the Great Wall of China is visible from outer space. It is, in fact, too thin to be noticed from such a great distance. The only two man-made structures visible from space are the Pyramids of Giza and the Hoover Dam.

Mirror Image

Only one of these pictures is an exact mirror image of the first one. Can you spot it?

66 As men get older, the toys get more expensive. 99

MARVIN DAVIS

💡 The first TV remote control was designed by the Zenith Radio Corporation in 1950. It worked using a cable that ran from the device to the TV set and was named 'Lazy Bones'.

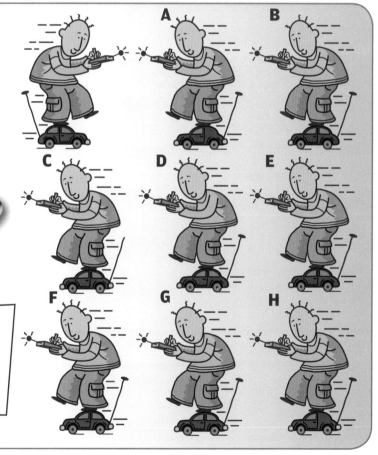

A **B**
C **D** **E**
F **G** **H**

Fill the Hole

The columns and rows that make up the finished grid have certain properties in common. Identify these matching qualities and you should be able to work out which of the squares below will correctly complete the grid.

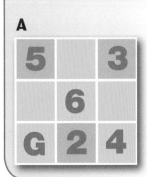

💡 Tin cans as a means of storing food were invented in 1810. Not until 1846 was the process widely adopted and it would be another 12 years before the can opener was invented.

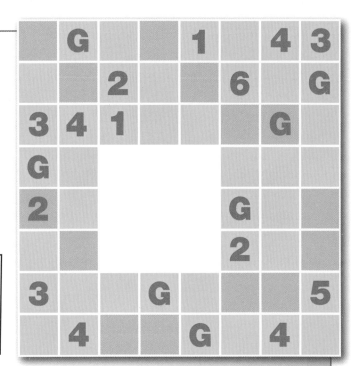

A

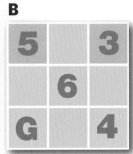

B

C

D

Number Combination

The numbers by each row and column describe black squares and groups of black squares that are adjoining. Colour in all the black squares and a six number combination will be revealed.

💡 The red and white national flags of Monaco and Indonesia are identical, except for the ratio.

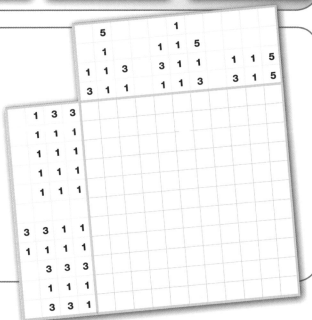

"A soldier will fight long and hard for a bit of coloured ribbon."

NAPOLEON BONAPARTE

Flagged Up!

In the sequence below, which of the alternatives, A, B, C or D, should replace the question mark?

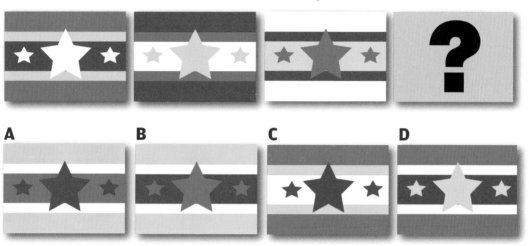

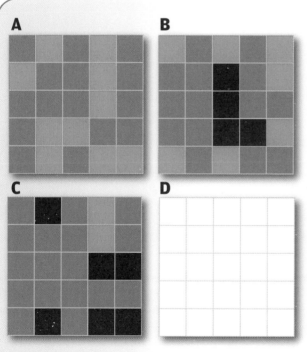

All Change

The colours of each square in pattern B are directly related to the colours in pattern A. The square colours in pattern C relate to pattern B the same way. Can you apply the same rules and fill in pattern D?

"I never travel without my diary. One should always have something sensational to read on the train." OSCAR WILDE

 Ghana's Lake Volta is the largest reservoir in the world.

Boats and Buoys

Every buoy has one boat found horizontally or vertically adjacent to it. No boat can be in an adjacent square to another boat (even diagonally). The numbers by each row and column tell you how many boats are there. Can you locate all the boats?

BUOY

BOAT

💡 Istanbul in Turkey is the only city in the world that resides on two continents. Straddling Europe and Asia, the city is divided by the Bosphorus Strait.

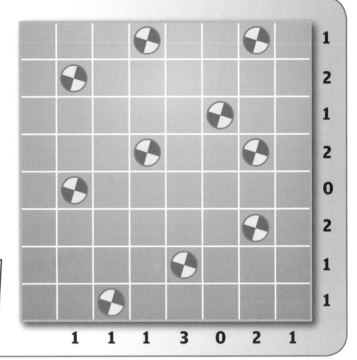

Bits and Pieces

These ten pieces can be arranged to spell out a three-figure number. Can you piece it together?

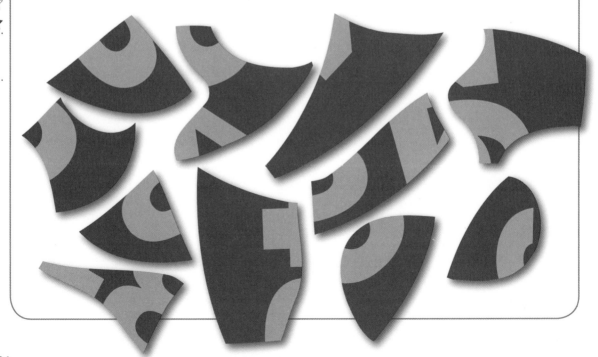

It's Your Turn

Playing the game of boxes, each player takes it in turns to join two adjacent dots with a line. If a player's line completes a box, the player wins the box and has another chance. It's your turn in the game below. To avoid giving your opponent a lot of boxes, what's your best move?

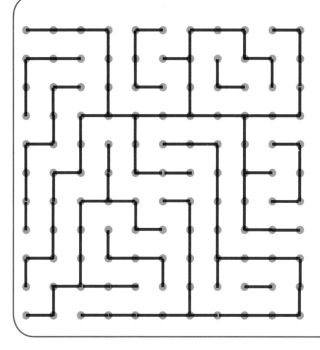

💡 In December 1953, Marilyn Monroe appeared on the cover of *Playboy* as 'Sweetheart of the Month'. It was the very first issue of the magazine.

Ball Recall

Study this image for a minute, cover it up with a sheet of paper and then answer the five questions below.

💡 Despite being extremely rare in reality there have been several recent films which use amnesia or memory loss as a motif, including *Eternal Sunshine of the Spotless Mind*, *Memento*, *Spirited Away*, *The Bourne Trilogy* and *Finding Nemo*.

Questions:
1. What is the total of the even numbered balls?
2. What is the total of the red, yellow and blue balls?
3. Which two balls can you see most of?
4. Which ball can you see least of?
5 Subtract the far left ball from the green ball.

DIFFICULTY ☆ ★ ★ ✏

Number Sweep

Colour in the squares until all the numbers are surrounded by the correct number of shaded squares. When the puzzles is correctly solved the shaded squares will reveal a number!

1	3		5		4		2		4		5		4	
3		6		6		4		4		5		7		4
	7		5		4		5		6		5		8	
5		6		4		4		3		3		6		5
	8		4		4		4		3		5		7	
5		6		5		7		3		5		7		3
	8		3		5		6		5		7		3	
4		6		5		7		6		8		6		2
	5		6		6		6		8		7		5	
1		4		5		3		3		5		5		3

💡 Octopuses collect crustacean shells and other objects from the ocean in order to build fortresses, or 'gardens', around their lairs.

DIFFICULTY ☆ ★ ★ ✏ 📄

Price Puzzle

Shopping for a present for your grandmother, you find yourself in a shop devoted to tea, which she loves. You buy a teapot and six cups, together with some teabags and spoons. You spent exactly 50 pounds. Can you work out how many boxes of teabags and spoons you bought?

1.99

17.15

2.95

1.30

💡 96% of all cups of tea drunk in the UK are brewed using tea bags.

❝All well-regulated families set apart an hour every morning for tea and bread and butter.❞ JOHN ADDISON

Macaw Mathematics

These symbols represent the numbers 1 to 4. If the purple parrot represents the number 2, can you work out what the other colour parrots are representing and make a working sum?

66 Teach a parrot the terms 'supply and demand' and you've got an economist. 99

THOMAS CARLYLE

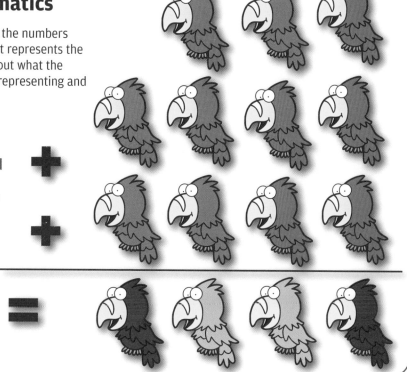

💡 Parrots are zygodactyls, meaning they have four toes on each foot – two pointing forwards, two pointing backwards.

Magic Squares

Complete the square using nine consecutive numbers, so that all rows, columns and large diagonals add up to the same total.

66 There are three kinds of lies: lies, damned lies, and statistics. 99

BENJAMIN DISRAELI

💡 The top-selling fiction writer of all time is Agatha Christie, the creator of the detectives Hercule Poirot and Miss Marple. Her 78 crime novels have sold an estimated two billion copies.

		14
	11	
8		

Loopy Numbers

Connect adjacent dots with either horizontal or vertical lines to create a continuous unbroken loop which never crosses over itself. Some, but not all of the boxes are numbered. The numbers in these boxes tell you how many sides of that box are used by your unbroken line.

💡 The International Criminal Police Organization, known as Interpol, has its headquarters in the French city of Lyons.

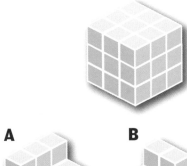

A Game of Two Halves

Which two shapes below will pair up to create the top shape?

❝Lies are essential to humanity. They are perhaps as important as the pursuit of pleasure and moreover are dictated by that pursuit.❞ MARCEL PROUST

💡 The first Superbowl half-time show in 1967 featured two marching bands from the universities of Michigan and Arizona – a far cry from today's showbiz spectacle.

A

B

C

D

E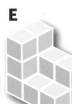

F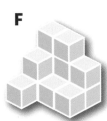

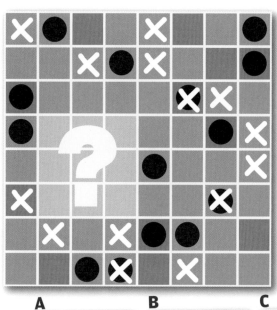

In the Hole

Which of the squares below correctly completes the grid?

"Only in men's imagination does every truth find an effective and undeniable existence. Imagination, not invention, is the supreme master of art as of life." JOSEPH CONRAD

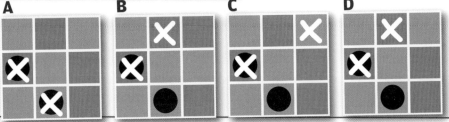

A   **B**   **C**   **D**

Troublesome Tiles

Below is a plan of a living room, showing fitted units that cannot be moved. Can you tile the whole floor using only the tile shown? The tiles are not reversible!

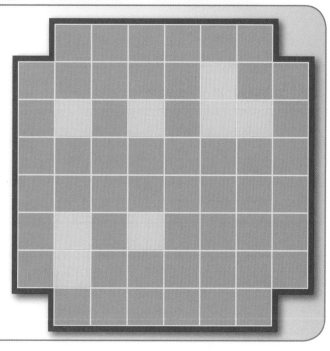

The term for the currency in Botswana is 'Pula' – meaning literally 'rain water'. Rain and water are both scarce in the landlocked southern African nation.

Beautiful Balloon

This balloon is made up of pink, green and cream panels, with no adjacent panels to be in the same colour. Can you work out what colour the marked panel should be?

?

> **My definition [of a philosopher] is of a man up in a balloon, with his family and friends holding the ropes which confine him to earth and trying to haul him down.** Louisa May Alcott

Hydrogen balloons were used by both sides during the US Civil War for aerial reconnaissance missions.

Box of Bits

Which box has exactly the right bits to make the image of the weightlifter?

❝ Only actions give life strength; only moderation gives it charm. ❞

JEAN PAUL RICHTER

Arrows

Complete the grid by drawing an arrow in each box that points in any one of the eight compass directions (N, E, S, W, NE, NW, SE and SW). The numbers in the outside boxes in the finished puzzle will reflect the number of arrows pointing in their direction.

💡 'Billabong' is an Australian English word for an oxbow lake, a curved stagnant pool of water attached to a waterway.

1	0	0	2	1	1
0		↘	↙		0
0	↗	↙	↙	↑	0
2		←		→	1
2	↖			↖	1
1	2	0	0	1	1

Find Your Way

Each colour represents a different direction. Starting in the middle die of the grid, follow the instructions correctly and you will visit every die in turn once only. What's the last die you visit on your trip?

Orange = Left
Black = Right
Green = Down
Purple = Up
Pink = Up Right
Red = Down Right
Yellow = Up Left
Blue = Down Left

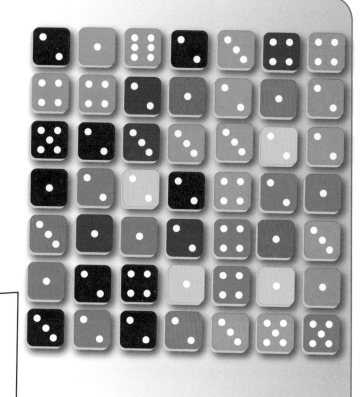

💡 In 1985, Blondie's Debbie Harry was immortalized in a set of rock 'n' roll stamps issued in Gambia, Liberia, Mali and Tanzania. The 'Women of Rock' stamps also featured Connie Francis, Janis Joplin, Cyndi Lauper and Carly Simon.

A Question of Art

Can you crack the logical secret behind the numbers on the back of these paintings, and work out the number that should replace the question mark on the work by Matisse?

❝❝ Art is not a handicraft, it is the transmission of feeling the artist has experienced. ❞❞ Leo Nikolayevich Tolstoy

16 DALI

104 MONDRIAN

? MATISSE

35 EL GRECO

112 PICASSO

💡 In 1961, Henri Matisse's *Le Bateau* was hung upside down for 47 days in New York's Museum of Modern Art (MOMA) until a visitor pointed out the error.

Shuffle Box

Fill up the shuffle box so that each row, column and long diagonal contains a Jack, Queen, King and Ace of each suit.

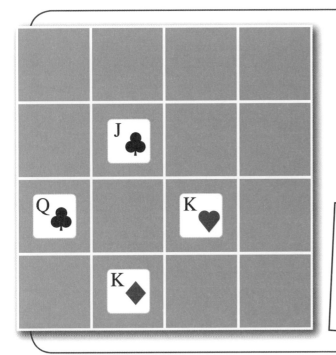

💡 The phrase 'mad as a hatter' pre-dates Lewis Carroll's memorable creation. His Mad Hatter reflected a real-life affliction as hat-makers had long been affected by mercury vapours – a chemical used during the process of curing felt. Prolonged exposure left many with nervous disorders and the symptoms of 'madness'.

💡 According to a 2007 survey the Honda Civic GX is the most environmentally friendly car on the market – just pipping the Toyota Prius.

Matching Pair

Only one of the tiles below is unique; the other 14 all have an exact matching pair. Can you find the one-off?

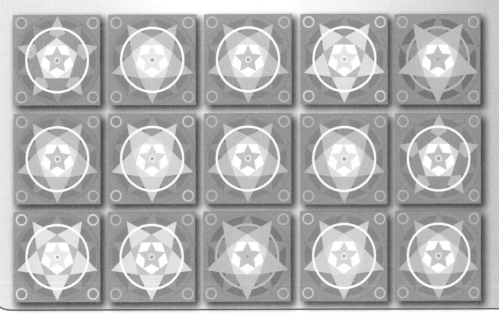

Think of a Number

At the Sea View guest house in Bournemouth, England, over the course of one week 459 breakfasts were served. 153 guests had a poached egg, 51 had a scrambled egg, 136 had cereal and 119 had fruit. What fraction of guests had an egg, and what fraction didn't?

💡 In 1906, the Battle Creek Toasted Corn Flakes Company, founded by W. K. Kellogg, began production of Kellogg's Corn Flakes – and a cereal dynasty was born.

Shape Shifting

Fill in the empty squares so that each row, column and long diagonal contains five different coloured stars.

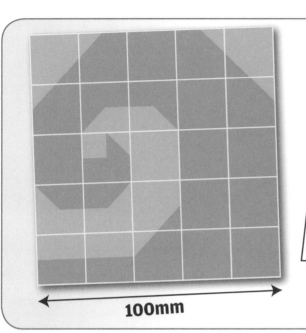

Size of the Wave

Can you work out the approximate area that this wave is occupying?

❝The wind and the waves are always on the side of the ablest navigator.❞ EDWARD GIBBON

💡 When a surfer is seen to be in the white foam of a wave after it has broken, he is said to be 'in the soup'.

100mm

Swan Scene

The four squares below can all be found in the picture grid; can you track them down? Beware, they may not be the right way up!

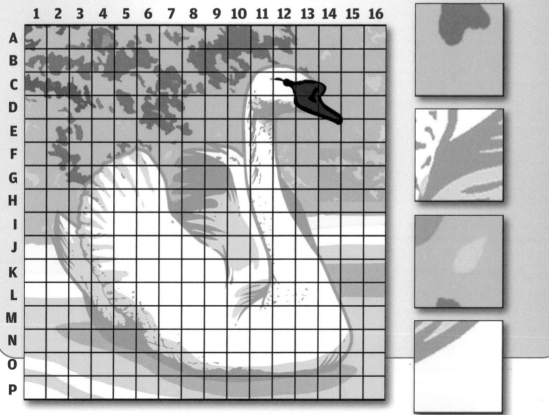

Building Blocks

Assuming all blocks that are not visible from this angle are present, how many blocks have been removed from this 6 x 6 x 6 cube?

❝We used to build civilizations. Now we build shopping malls.❞

BILL BRYSON

💡 Russian Alexey Pajitnov originally designed and programmed the video game Tetris in June 1985, while he was working for the Dorodnicyn Computing Centre of the Academy of Science in Moscow, USSR.

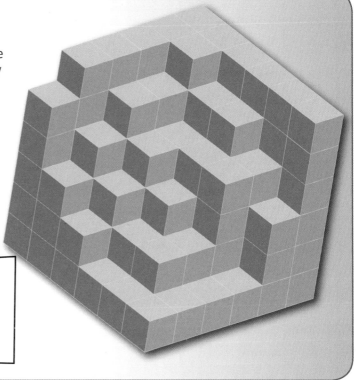

Codoko Six

Complete the first grid so that every row and column contain all the letters M, A, G, L, K and I. Do the same with grid 2 and the numbers 1, 2, 3, 4, 5 and 6. To decode the finished grid, add the numbers in the shaded squares to the letters in the matching squares in the second (ie: A + 3 = D, Y + 4 = C) to get six new letters, which can be arranged to spell the name of a world city.

	M			A	
M				I	
A		K			
			A		G
G		L		M	
	K		M		I

		3		6	
5					3	4
3		6			
		1			5	2
		5	1		3
	2			4	

Coloured Cap Capers

Five caps – three blue and two red – are in a box. Three clever kids, Janet, Jules and Jim know exactly how many caps of each colour are in there. Someone turns the light off in the room so it is completely dark. Then they each select a cap, put it on and close the box. When the light is turned back on, each can see the others two caps, but not their own. Janet says she can't work out what colour her cap is, and Jules says she can't either, at which point, Jim says "I know!" What colour is Jim's hat? And by the way... Jim is blindfolded.

66 If anybody says he can think about quantum physics without getting giddy, that only shows he has not understood the first thing about them. 99 Niels Bohr

Colour Amaze

Find a path from one white square to the other. You may only pass from a green square to a red one, a red to a yellow, a yellow to a blue or a blue to a green, and you may not travel diagonally.

66 The charm of history and its enigmatic lesson consist in the fact that, from age to age, nothing changes and yet everything is completely different. 99 Aldous Huxley

Denmark is the most taxed nation in the world. Its highest rate of income tax is 68 percent, with the basic rate starting at 42 percent.

Shape Stacker

Can you work out the logic behind the numbers in these shapes, and the total of A + B?

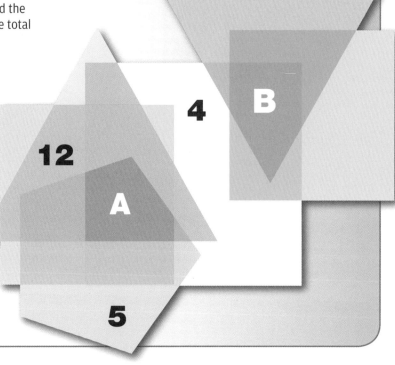

> **Physical bravery is an animal instinct; moral bravery is much higher and truer courage.**
> WENDELL PHILLIPS

It takes 1,851 gallons of water to refine one barrel (42 gallons) of crude oil.

Pool Poser

You're playing stripes in a game of pool, and you've cleaned up all your balls. You're snookered on the black though . . . Can you spot the shot?

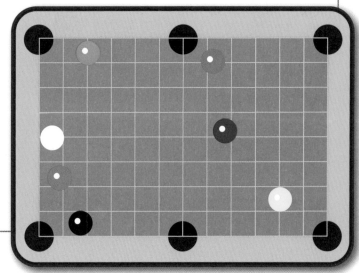

George Henry Sutton, of Toledo, Ohio, had no hands, yet won a national billiard championship, and he once made a consecutive run of 3,000 balls.

Rounders We Go

Which of the wheels: A, B, C or D, is missing from the set above?

66 The key to change... is to let go of fear. 99

Rosanne Cash

💡 The six-day war between El Salvador and Honduras in July 1969 is popularly known as 'La guerra del fútbol' or 'Football War', although football was not at the root of the conflict.

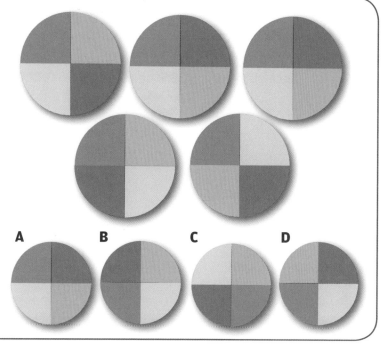

A   B   C   D

Jeep Jumble

Only two of these pictures are exactly the same. Can you spot the matching pair?

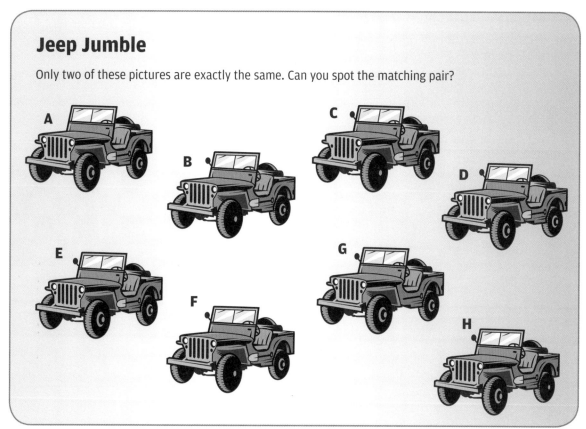

SOLUTIONS

1:

2 1 2 1 0 1 2 1

0 3 1 0 2 1 1 2

2: Each vertical and horizontal line contains one purple, one yellow and one white outer box. Each line also contains one purple inner diamond and two yellow ones. Finally each line contains one purple star and two yellow ones. The missing image should be a yellow outer box with a purple inner diamond and a yellow star.

3: 5,000 square millimetres. Each 20 x 20 square represents 400cm². 12 and a half squares are used.

4:

J ♥	Q ♣	K ♠	A ♦
K ♦	A ♠	J ♣	Q ♥
A ♣	K ♥	Q ♦	J ♠
Q ♠	J ♦	A ♥	K ♣

5:

B	D	C	A
C	A	B	D
A	C	D	B
D	B	A	C

6: A is the odd shape out.

7: £9,075. 1st bet wins £140, + your bet back = £150. Second bet is £75 and wins £1,050 + your bet = £1,125 Third bet is £562.50 and wins £7,875 + your bet = £8,437.50 Add the £75 you kept from your first bet, and the £562.50 you kept from your second and your winnings are £9,075.00.

8:

9:

10: He took the test. On reaching into the bag, he drew out a piece of paper and ate it before anyone could see what was on it. The other piece of paper carried a cross, of course, so the one he had eaten must have had a tick on it, right? Well, that's what the crowd believed, and that's what mattered.

11: 360. The numbers represent the number of sides in the shape they occupy. When shapes overlap, the numbers are multiplied. 3 x 4 x 5 x 6 = 360.

12: Last tile on the middle row.

13:

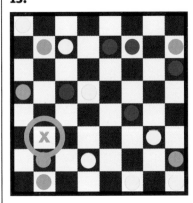

14: B.

15: 4,950 square millimetres. Each 20 x 20 square represents 400cm². 6 squares, 3 half-square triangles, 2 half-squares, 9 quarter squares and 13 eighth-square triangles are used.

16: A red house with the light on. Two houses the same colour are followed by one with the light on, two houses with different lighting (off and on) are followed by a red house.

17:
1. 3.
2. 2.
3. Japan. Red circle, white background.
4. 4: white, red, blue and yellow.
5. Orange and black.

18:

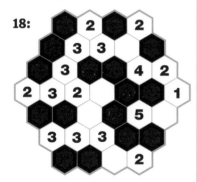

19: They ended their walk on the bench at square 1C. The only square they didn't visit was 5C, which is in the middle of the pond.

20:

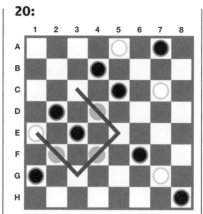

21:
Green 1.
Orange 2.
Black 3.
Blue 4.

22:

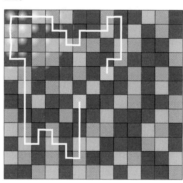

23:

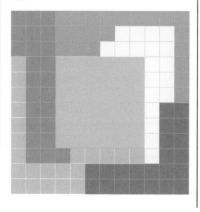

24

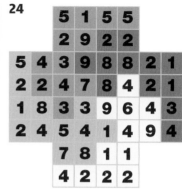

25:

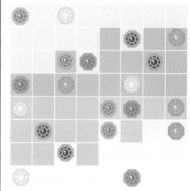

26: Van Gogh.

27: B and F.

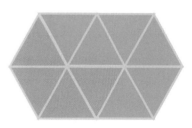

28: Green.

29: A.

30:

31: D and E are the pair.

32: b) 18 a) 16 c) 15 d) 14.

33: Each vertical and horizontal line contains one shape with a red outline and two shapes with a black outline. Each line also contains one shape where the inner quartered circle has been removed and one shape that has been rotated through 90 degrees. The missing shape should not be rotated, it should have a red outline and the inner circle should be missing.

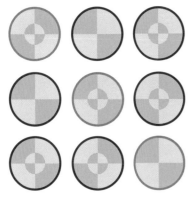

34: L5, D11, F1, F10.

35:

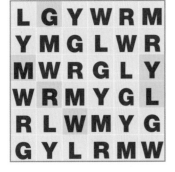

G + 6 = M   L + 3 = O   Y + 1 = Z   W + 4 = A   M + 5 = R   R + 2 = T
Solution: Mozart

36: Each pentagon contains numbers that add up to 30. The sides nearest adjoining pentagons all add up to 10.

37: 2. Add all the pink numbers and divide the total by the highest pink number. Do the same with the yellow numbers.
HUB 1: Pink: 4 + 3 + 3 + 5 = 15, ÷ 5 = 3. Yellow: 2 + 3 + 3 + 4 = 12, ÷ 4 = 3
HUB 2: Pink: 4 + 3 + 2 + 9 = 18, ÷ 2 = 2. Yellow: 1 + 2 + 4 + 7 = 14, ÷ 2 = 2.

38: Pig = 8, Piglet = 5, Chicken = 4, Chick = 2, Egg = 1. Seven chicks are required.

39: F and H.

40: A.

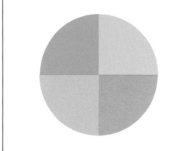

41: A. With each new image, the bottom row of dots moves to the top before the corner colours are swapped with their diagonal opposites.

42:
1. 3.
2. Top left.
3. X.
4. 4.
5. 13.

43: ?=23.

2
4
6
9

44: H.

45:

46:

4	2	3	3	2	0
3	X	O	O	O	3
4	X	X	O	O	3
2	O	O	X	O	2
4	O	X	X	X	3
1	4	3	4	3	4

47:

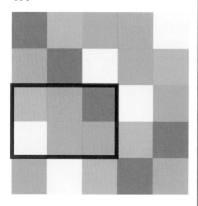

48: 1 watermelon (4.85), 3 pineapples (6.84), 4 bananas (1.80) and 3 oranges (1.26)
4.85 + 6.84 + 1.80 + 1.26 = 14.75.

49:

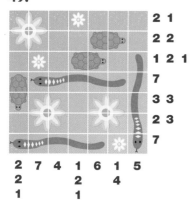

50: A.

51: Red.

52:

53:

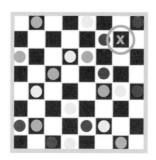

54: Samantha, Jennifer, Jessica, Elizabeth, Hannah, Michelle, Julia, Grace, Angela and Monica.

55: 25. Kaplutski has solved 12 cases and Wojowitz has solved 13. Multiply both numbers by four to get a percentage.

56: 48 percent is blue, 52 percent is orange. 12 out of 25 triangles that make up the shape are blue, 13 are orange. Multiply both numbers by 4 and you see a percentage.

57:

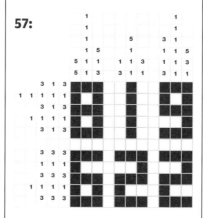

58: 1,008. The numbers represent the number of sides in the shape they occupy. When shapes overlap, the numbers are multiplied.
A: 3 x 4 x 4 x 6 = 288
B: 3 x 3 x 4 x 4 x 5 = 720
288 + 720 = 1,008.

59: 80. Multiply the alphabetical position of the first letter of each name by the number of vowels it contains. T = 20 and Tom Cruise contains 4 vowels. 20 x 4 = 80.

60:

61: C.

62: 30% is grey, 70% is green. 12 out of 40 triangles in the shape are grey, 28 are green. Multiply both numbers by 2.5 and you see a percentage.

63: 10. Add the top and front faces and divide by 2. Then multiply by the front face.

64:

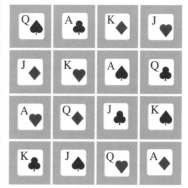

65:

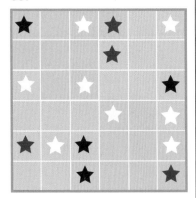

66:

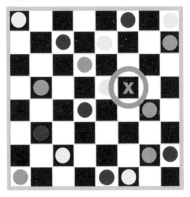

67:

68: From the lower square to the higher one, the direction of movement each colour indicates is: Green-Up, Orange-Left, Blue-Right, Purple-Down.

69: Blue.

70:

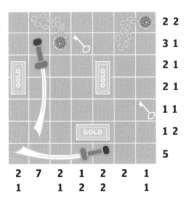

71:

72: D.

73: 54. Add the three largest white numbers together and multiply by the smallest. 7 + 6 + 5 = 18 x 3 = 54.

74:
A) 6. Multiply opposite numbers and add up the integers of the total.
B) 14. Add the integers in opposite numbers.

75:

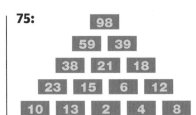

76:

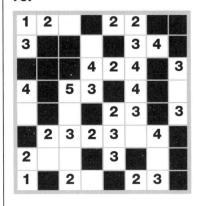

77: C and I are the pair.

78: 4,750 square millimetres. Each 20 x 20 square represents 400cm^2.
10 squares, 4 half squares, 1 quarter square and 5 eighth triangles are used, and subtract four quarter square windows.

79:

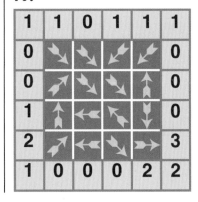

80: Tom Cruise.

81:

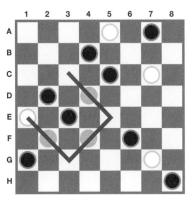

82:

83:

1	1	1	1			
4	2	2	2	2	6	
1	2	3	3	3	3	2	2
2	3	4	7	4	4	3	1
3	4	0	3	9	5	4	2
2	1	0	4	1	3	1	2
1	7	7	1	4	1		
1	8	2	0			

84: C.

85: The jewels are in the cab in square 5d.

86: 6. Multiply the right face and the front face and subtract the top one.

87: C and D.

88:

89: From the lower square to the higher one, the direction of movement each colour indicates is: Green-Up, Pink-Left, Orange-Right, Blue-Down.

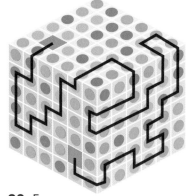

90: E.

91:

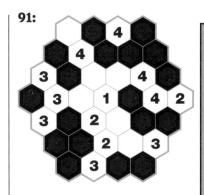

92: J and D.

93: C and F.

94:

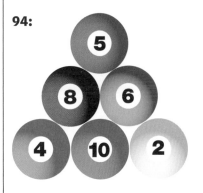

95:

96:

97: He lent them a boat. With 18 boats, Manuela can have 9, Maria can have 6 and Monica can have 2, thus fulfilling their father's will. 9 + 6 + 2 = 17, so following the division of the fleet, they are able to return the fisherman's boat.

98: A2, G2, L1, O5.

99:

100:

3	4	3	2	3	1
3	X	O	O	O	3
4	X	O	O	O	2
5	X	X	X	X	5
3	O	X	O	X	3
1	5	3	4	4	3

101: A and E are the pair.

102: D.

103:

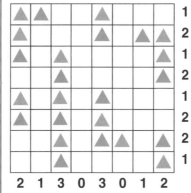

104: H.

105: Lilac.

106: 11 and 10. The total of the numbers in each section is the reverse of the total of the opposite section. 23 and 32. 38 and 83 etc.

107: Each pentagon contains numbers that add up to 30. The sides nearest adjoining pentagons are the numbers 1 to 12 in order.

108: 24. Score one for a consonant and two for a vowel, then multiply the totals together. 4 x 6 = 24.

109: A. The main outer shape swaps colour with the shape just inside it. The inner shape swaps colour with the outside shapes. The four small shapes move from the second shape to the outside one.

110: 3,650 square millimetres. Each 20 x 20 square represents 400cm2. 4 squares, 6 half squares, 2 half-square triangles, 3 quarter-squares and 3 8th of a square triangles are used.

111:

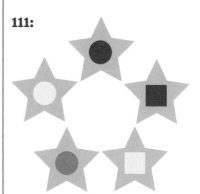

112: b) 15 c) 12 d) 10 a) 8.

113: C and I are the pair.

114: A and C.

115:
A) 8. Subtract the numbers opposite each other.
B) 18. Add the opposite numbers.

116: B. Each row and column in the grid contains four dark and three light squares, and numbers that total 10.

117:

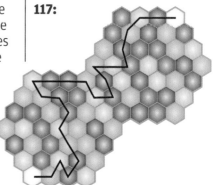

118:

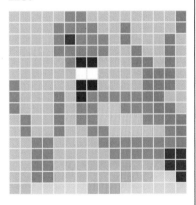

119: G is the odd one out.

120:
Pink = Left
Red = Right
Black = Down
Yellow = Up
Purple = Up Right
Brown = Down Right
Blue = Up Left
Green = Down Left.
The final die in your trip is the red 4, sixth die down in the second column.

121:

2	1	6	3	4	5
3	2	5	4	1	6
4	3	2	6	5	1
1	4	3	5	6	2
6	5	4	1	2	3
5	6	1	2	3	4

122:
1. 5.
2. Green.
3. 0.
4. 1.
5. Green.

123:

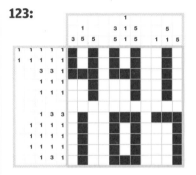

124:

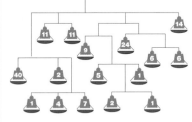

125: Cleopatra.

126: A red 2. Two numbers the same are followed by a red number. Two numbers of different colours are followed by a 2.

127:

128:

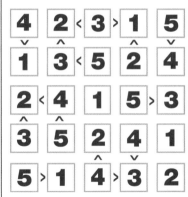

129: The boat finishes the race at the buoy in square 4C.

130: A and F are the pair.

131:

132: Originally, the men paid £30, but they each got £1 back, so they have only paid £27. £25 of this went into the driver's cash box while £2 went into his pocket.

133: B

134:

109

135: Mozart.

136: A and E are the pair.

137:

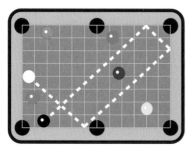

138: A.

139:

140: A, C, and E.

141: Ziplock is alien G.

142: Thumper had 50 and Cottontail had 30.

143: D.

144: E.

145: C. Each row and column in the grid contains two green squares and a letter B, and numbers that total 8.

146:

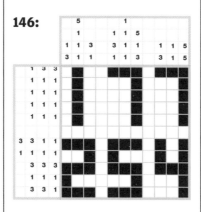

147: A. With each new image, the stars take the colour of the previous double stripes. The double stripes take the colour of the previous background, the background takes the colour of the previous central stripe and the central stripe takes the colour of the previous stars.

148: If its bordering squares (not diagonals) are predominantly purple, a square becomes purple. If they are predominantly orange it becomes orange. If the bordering cell colours are equal in number, the square becomes black and if the bordering squares have now become predominantly black, a square also becomes black.

149:

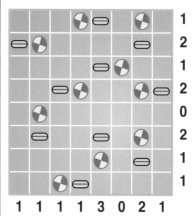

150: 948.

151: A line on the left or right of this square will only give up one box to your opponent.

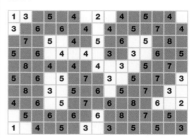

152:
1. 14.
2. 15.
3. Red and yellow.
4. 4.
5. 3.

153:

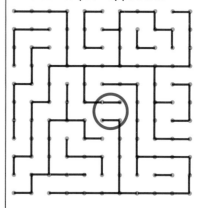

154: Four spoons and five boxes of teabags.

155:
Pink 1.
Purple 2.
Red 3.
Green 4.

156:

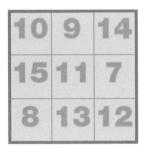

157:

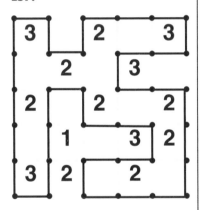

158: D and B.

159: D. Each row and column in the grid contains 2 pink squares, 2 black dots and two white Xs.

160:

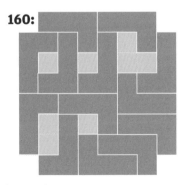

161: Cream.

162: B.

163:

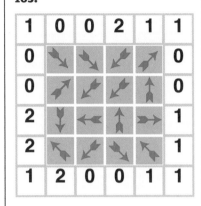

164:
The final die in your trip is the red 4, top die in the sixth column.

165: 91. Take the alphabetical position of the first letter of the city, and multiply by the number of letters in the word. 13 (M) x 7 = 91.

166:

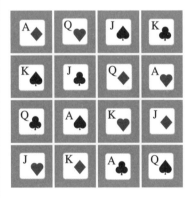

167: Second tile on the bottom row.

168: 4/9ths did, and 5/9ths didn't. 1/9th of 459 is 51. 4 x 51 is 204 (153 + 51) and 5 x 51 is 255 (136 + 119).

169:

170: 6,950 square inches. Each 20 x 20 square represents 400 square inches. 9 squares, 11 half squares, 5 quarter squares and 13 eighth-square triangles are used.

171: E8, L11, F7, K2.

172: 75.

173:

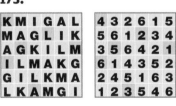

G + 5 = L   I + 6 = O   M + 1 = N
A + 3 = D   K + 4 = O   L + 2 = N
Solution: LONDON

111

174: Blue. If Jules and Jim were both wearing red caps, Janet would know hers was blue, and similarly if Janet and Jim were both in red caps, Jules would know hers was blue. So when Janet says she can't work out which colour her cap is, that means that Jules and Jim are either both wearing blue caps, or that they have one of each. Assuming Jules has worked this out, if she sees Jim in a red cap, she will know hers must be blue. If she cannot work out her own cap colour, Jim's cap must also be blue.

175:

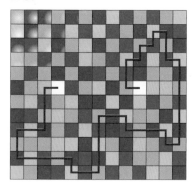

176: 288. The numbers represent the number of sides in the shape they occupy. When shapes overlap, the numbers are multiplied.
A: 3 x 4 x 4 x 5 = 240.
B: 4 x 4 x 3 = 48.

177:

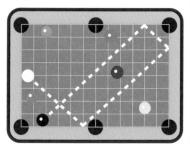

178: C.

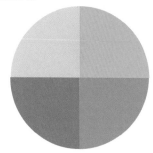

179: B and F are the pair.

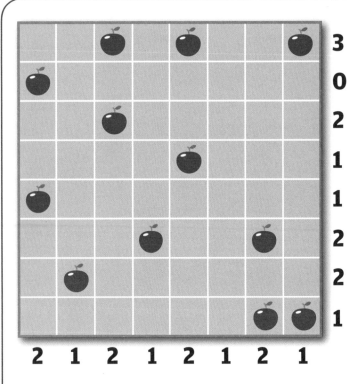

3
0
2
1
1
2
2
1

2 1 2 1 2 1 2 1

Apples and Pears

Every apple has one pear found horizontally or vertically adjacent to it. No pear can be in an adjacent square to another pear (even diagonally). The numbers by each row and column tell you how many pears there are. Can you locate all the pears?

66All human history attests that happiness for man, the hungry sinner! Since Eve ate apples, much depends on dinner.99

LORD BYRON

APPLE   **PEAR**

💡 Over 7,500 varieties of apples are grown throughout the world. In 2006-7 the People's Republic of China led the world in commercial apple production, with almost 27 million tons, followed by the United States, with almost five million tons. In 2006-7, commercial world production of apples was over 48 million tons.

What's Coming Next?

The sequence below follows a logical pattern. Can you work out the colour and shape next in line?

?

💡 US President Ronald Reagan was such a huge baseball fan that he worked as a radio announcer for the Chicago Cubs - a job that provided him with a springboard into acting.

Kitchen Capers

One of these pictures of Pierre the chef is an exact mirror image of the first one. Can you spot which one?

❝Great eaters and great sleepers are incapable of anything else that is great.❞ HENRY IV OF FRANCE

💡 The world's most expensive sandwich, created by London chef Scott McDonald, costs $170. Its ingredients are Wagyu beef, fresh lobe foie gras, black truffle mayonnaise, brie de meaux, arugula, red pepper and mustard confit and plum tomatoes.

Knight's Move

Find an empty square in the grid that is one chess knight's move away from a blue, red and yellow circle. A knight's move is an 'L' shape – two squares sideways, up or down in any direction, followed by one square to the left or right.

❝I failed to make the chess team because of my height.❞
WOODY ALLEN

💡 In 1980, after 24 hours and 30 minutes, consisting of 193 moves, Yedael Stepak beat Yaakov Mashian in the world's longest decided chess game.

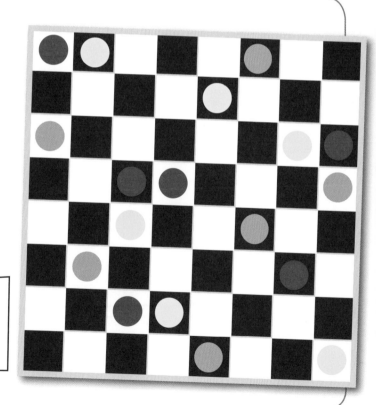

Honeycomb Halves

Sydney is a keen beekeeper and he is collecting his prized honeycomb to sell at the village fair. He is trying to ensure that each parcel is exactly the same. Which two honeycomb shapes shown below will pair up to create the top shape?

> **The men of experiment are like the ant; they only collect and use. But the bee . . . gathers its materials from the flowers of the garden and of the field, but transforms and digests it by a power of its own.**
>
> LEONARDO DA VINCI

A

B

C

D

E

F

Honeybees can direct other bees to food by dancing. The movements tell them the location and direction of the food.

Ticket to Ride

These 10 pieces of a train ticket can be assembled to spell the name of a world city... which one?

💡 According to the chronicler Raphael Holinshed, there were an estimated 72,000 executions carried out in England during the reign of Henry VIII – including two of his wives.

Star Spotter

Three stars can be seen in different directions in the night sky. Can you find out what star type they all are, where they can be found and where we should be looking?

• Ipson 7 is not in the constellation of Orion, nor is it a white dwarf star. It can be seen in the west.
• The neutron star can be seen in the east. It is not Jalafrey 2.
• Zan 10 can be found in the constellation of Capricorn.

	Taurus	Orion	Capricorn	Red Dwarf	White Dwarf	Neutron	East	West	North
Ipson 7									
Jalafrey 2									
Zan 10									
East						
West						
North						
Red Dwarf			
White Dwarf			
Neutron			

💡 In 1963, Russian Valentina Vladimirovna Tereshkova became the first woman to enter space as a crew member of *Vostok 6*.

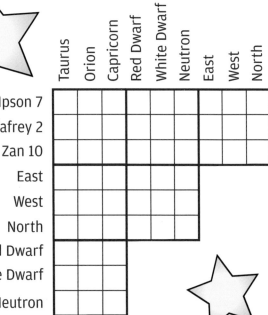

Will It Fit?

Black Beard the pirate has a big wooden box measuring four metres wide, three metres deep and three metres high. His 10 centimetre wide mast has broken into two pieces, one five metres long and one five and a half metres long. Can he get either, neither or both of the pieces into the box?

❝A stone thrown at the right time is better than gold given at the wrong time.❞ PERSIAN PROVERB

💡 The world's largest coral reef ecosystem, the Great Barrier Reef, is home to approximately 1,500 species of fish, 400 species of corals, 4,000 species of molluscs, 500 species of seaweed, 215 species of birds, 16 species of sea snake and six species of sea turtle.

Shape Shifting

Fill in the empty squares so that each row, column and long diagonal contains five different symbols.

❝Man must shape his tools lest they shape him.❞ ARTHUR MILLER

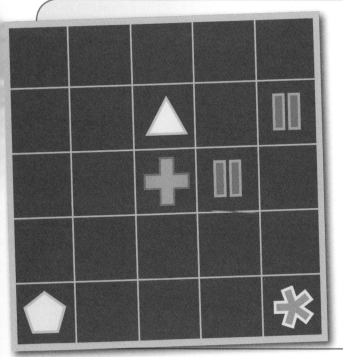

💡 The Nintendo Game Boy is the world's most popular videogame system. Between 1989 and 2000 more than 100 million units were sold.

Odd One Out!

Which of the shapes below is not the same as the other ones?

66 All that we are is the result of what we have thought. If a man speaks or acts with an evil thought, pain follows him. If a man speaks or acts with a pure thought, happiness follows him, like a shadow that never leaves him. **99** BUDDHA

💡 The quiz show *Deal or No Deal*, in which contestants try to win money randomly concealed within identical sealed boxes, was created by Dutch producers Endemol and has been syndicated in over 40 countries all over the world.

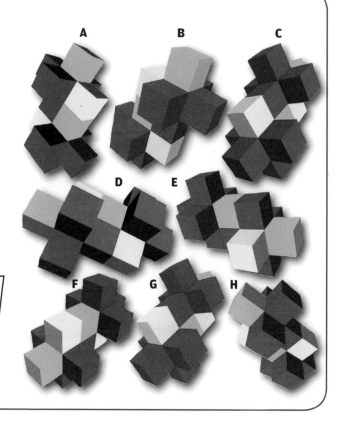

A   B   C   D   E   F   G   H

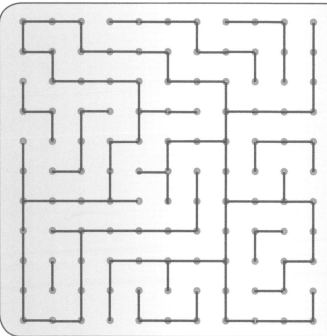

It's Your Turn

Playing the game of boxes, each player takes it in turns to join two adjacent dots with a line. If a player's line completes a box, the player wins the box and has another go. It's your turn in the game, left. To avoid giving your opponent a lot of boxes, what's your best move?

66 Man should forget his anger before he lies down to sleep. **99**

MOHANDAS GANDHI

💡 COGS is also commonly used as an acronym in accounting. Standing for Cost of Goods Sold, it allows for the calculation of gross profit.

Revolutions

Cog A has 16 teeth, cog B has 10 and cog C has eight. How many revolutions must cog A turn through to make the letters the right way up on all three cogs?

❝ Talent wins games, but teamwork and intelligence wins championships. ❞

MICHAEL JORDAN

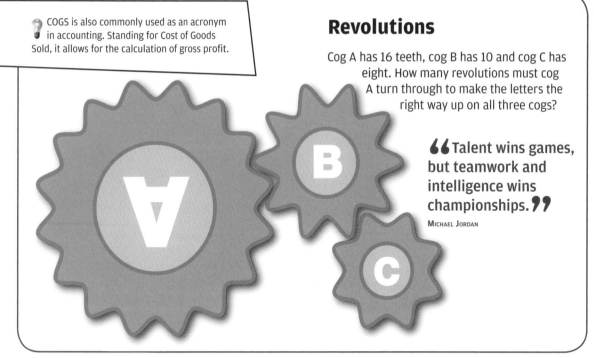

Radio Signals

In the sequence below, which of the numbered alternatives, A, B, C or D, should replace the question mark?

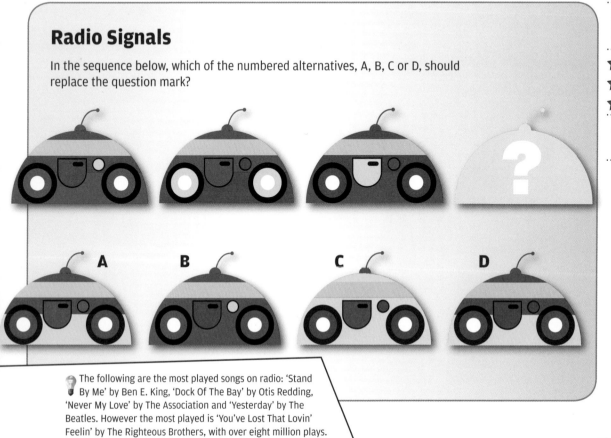

💡 The following are the most played songs on radio: 'Stand By Me' by Ben E. King, 'Dock Of The Bay' by Otis Redding, 'Never My Love' by The Association and 'Yesterday' by The Beatles. However the most played is 'You've Lost That Lovin' Feelin'' by The Righteous Brothers, with over eight million plays.

Nice Moves!

To complete Lionel's world renowned dance move, all the steps below must be taken in the correct order. What is the first step to be taken in the dance sequence?

FINISH!

💡 The original name of belly dance is *Raqs Sharqi*, which means 'Dance of the Orient'. In France, it got dubbed *danse du ventre*, which literally means "belly dance" due to the flutter of the dancer's stomach. It is believed that belly dancing was created to help prepare women for birth.

"To be fond of dancing was a certain step towards falling in love." JANE AUSTEN

Weigh To Go

The coloured balls represent the numbers 1, 2, 3, 4 and 5. Can you work out which one is which, and therefore how many blue balls are required to balance the final scale?

66 Charity is no substitute for justice withheld. 99

SAINT AUGUSTINE

💡 Every cubic foot of water weighs about 64 pounds. Only 2.5 percent of the water on the earth is not salty. Of this, only about 0.3 percent is available for drinking. The rest is trapped in ice and groundwater.

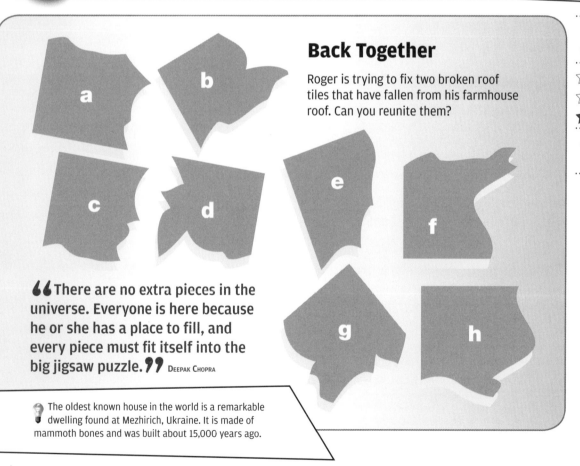

Back Together

Roger is trying to fix two broken roof tiles that have fallen from his farmhouse roof. Can you reunite them?

66 There are no extra pieces in the universe. Everyone is here because he or she has a place to fill, and every piece must fit itself into the big jigsaw puzzle. 99 DEEPAK CHOPRA

💡 The oldest known house in the world is a remarkable dwelling found at Mezhirich, Ukraine. It is made of mammoth bones and was built about 15,000 years ago.

Equal Shapes

Cut a straight line through this shape to create two shapes that are identical.

💡 Charlie Chaplin once won third prize in a Charlie Chaplin look-alike contest.

Round in Circles

Draw a single continuous line around the grid that passes through all the circles. The line must enter and leave each box in the centre of one of its four sides.

Black Circle: Turn left or right in the box, and the line must pass straight through the next and previous boxes.
White Circle: Travel straight through the box, and the line must turn in the next and/or previous box.

💡 British inventor Sir Charles Fothergill Wheatstone coined the term 'microphone' in 1827. A musical man, he also invented the accordian two years later.

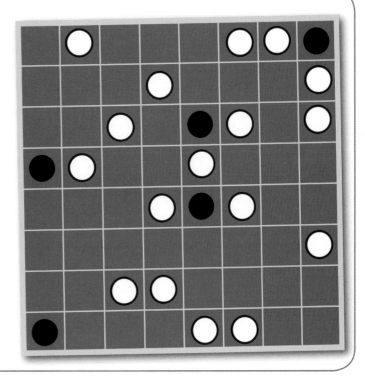

Sudoku

Complete the grid so that all rows and columns, and each outlined block of nine squares, contain the numbers 1, 2, 3, 4, 5, 6, 7, 8 and 9.

8		9	6	1	4			3
	2				9	6	7	
5		3	7				4	
		6	9		7	4	8	5
4	3							
7			8		6	3		
9		1	2			8		6
6		7			3		2	
	5		4		8	7		1

💡 Every four days the world's population increases by one million people.

❝Three grand essentials to happiness in this life are something to do, something to love, and something to hope for.❞

Joseph Addison

Find the Letter

What letter, in what colour, should replace the red question mark so that the grid follows a pattern?

❝Honesty is the first chapter in the book of wisdom.❞

Thomas Jefferson

💡 Between 1848 and 1852, at the height of the brief Gold Rush period, the population of California swelled from 14,000 to 223,000. In 1850 California officially became a state.

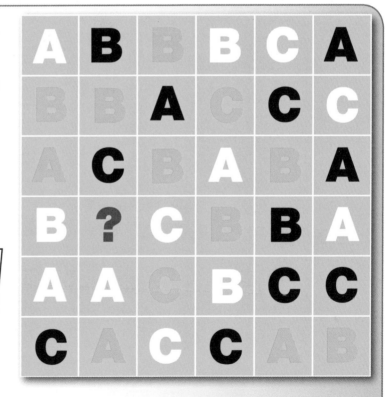

Sum Total

Replace the question marks with mathematical symbols (+, -, x or ÷) to make the equation.

$$35 \; ? \; 7 \; ? \; 4 \; ? \; 4 = 3$$

Salt and Pepper

Every salt shaker has a pepper mill found horizontally or vertically adjacent to it. No pepper mill can be in an adjacent square to another one (even diagonally). The numbers by each row and column tell you how many pepper mills are there. Can you locate all of them?

SALT

PEPPER

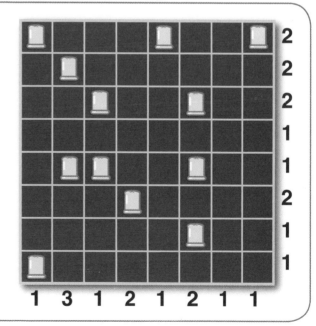

Come Together

Michael just has to fill the shape on the left to complete the tiling of his bathroom. Which two shapes below will pair up to finish the job?

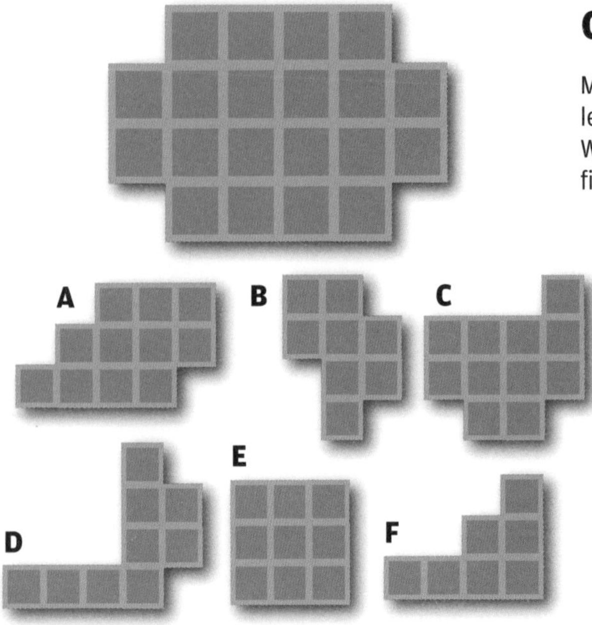

☆ **DIFFICULTY**
★
★
✏️

A **B** **C**

E

D **F**

❝The harder I work, the luckier I get. ❞ Samuel Goldwyn

💡 The world's largest rest room is in Chong Qing, China, and can support as many as 1,000 people using it at the same time. Additionally it offers radio and TV to entertain users of this mammoth rest room.

Where Next?

The arrows indicate whether a number in a box is greater or smaller than an adjacent number. Complete the grid so that all rows and columns contain the numbers 1 to 5.

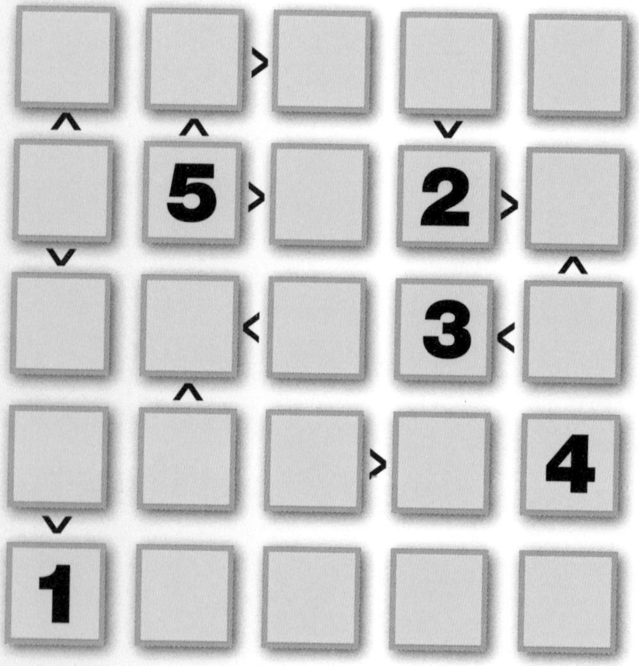

☆ **DIFFICULTY**
☆
★
✏️
📄

❝God loved the birds and invented trees. Man loved the birds and invented cages. ❞ Jacques Deval

💡 In one year, an acre of trees can absorb as much carbon as is produced by a car driven up to 8,700 miles.

Grid with clues: top row has `>` between columns 2–3, `v` between columns 4's area. Second row contains 5, `>`, 2, `>`. Third row contains `<`, 3, `<`. Fourth row contains `>`, 4. Fifth row contains 1.

Jiggery Pokery

Janet is struggling to finish the jigsaw; which of the four pieces shown below complete the jigsaw and make a perfect square?

❝A man who won't die for something is not fit to live.❞

MARTIN LUTHER KING JR

💡 John Spilsbury, a London engraver and mapmaker, produced the first jigsaw puzzle in around 1760. Spilsbury mounted one of his maps on a sheet of hardwood and cut around the borders of the countries using a fine-bladed saw. The end product was an educational pastime, designed as an aid in teaching children their geography. The idea caught on and, until about 1820, jigsaw puzzles remained primarily educational tools.

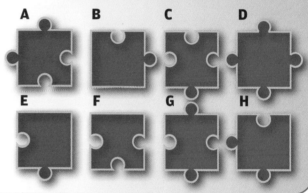

Squared Off!

Complete the grid so that every row and column, and every outlined area, contains the letters A, B, C, D, E and F.

❝When science finally locates the centre of the universe, some people will be surprised to learn they're not it.❞ BERNARD BAILEY

💡 The German philosopher Friedrich Nietzsche was also Professor of Classics at the University of Basel in Switzerland.

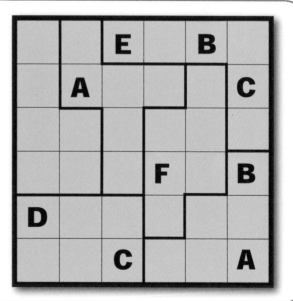

Pulley Puzzler

Turn the handle in the indicated direction...
Does the weight go up or down?

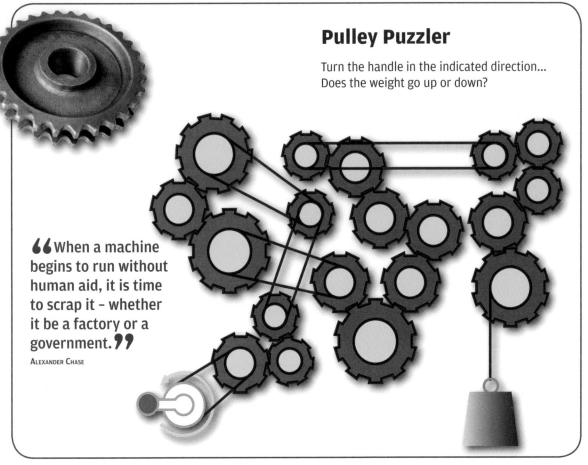

> ❝ When a machine begins to run without human aid, it is time to scrap it – whether it be a factory or a government. ❞
>
> ALEXANDER CHASE

Hidden Answer

The value of each shape is the number of sides each shape has, multiplied by the number within it. Thus a square containing the number 4 has a value of 16. Find a block of four squares (two squares wide by two squares high) with a total value of exactly 70.

> ❝ Hope never abandons you; you abandon it. ❞
>
> GEORGE WEINBERG

2			3	
3	0	1		2
3	1		0	3
			3		2
3	2	1	3	1

Loopy Numbers

Connect adjacent dots with either horizontal or vertical lines to create a continuous unbroken loop which never crosses over itself. Some but not all of the boxes are numbered. The numbers in these boxes tell you how many sides of that box are used by your unbroken line.

❝Friendship with oneself is all important because without it one cannot be friends with anybody else in the world.❞
ELEANOR ROOSEVELT

Hue Goes There?

Three of the sections below can be found in our main grid, one cannot. Can you spot the section that doesn't belong?

❝The artist must create a spark before he can make a fire and before art is born, the artist must be ready to be consumed by the fire of his own creation.❞ AUGUSTE RODIN

💡 The deepest part of the ocean is the Marina trench in the Pacific. It reaches a depth of 10,911 metres.

Next in Sequence

The sequence below follows a logical pattern. Can you work out the colour and shape next in line?

German composer Johannes Brahms was in his early forties before he composed his first symphony.

Noughts and Crosses

The numbers around the edge of the grid describe the number of X's in the vertical, horizontal and diagonal lines connecting with that square. Complete the grid so that there is an X or O in every square.

3	4	3	4	5	4	4
5			O	X		6
4				O		3
2		O				6
5	O				X	3
3			O	X		4
4	5	3	4	4	5	3

" He who postpones the hour of living is like the rustic who waits for the river to run out before he crosses. **"** HORACE

Formerly the residence of the Dali Lama, the Potala Palace in Tibet contains over 1,000 rooms and 10,000 individual shrines. It is 13 stories high and 360 metres in width. It is now a museum by decree of the Chinese government.

The Great Divide

Divide up the grid into four equally sized, equally shaped parts, each containing one each of the five coloured stars.

66 Failures are divided into two classes – those who thought and never did, and those who did and never thought. **99** JOHN CHARLES SALAK

Chocolate Chunks

This chocolate bar contains dark, white and milk chocolate segments. The manufacturers produce the bar to a strict patented pattern; are you able to work out which of the square chunks shown below correctly completes the bar?

66 There is nothing better than a friend, unless it is a friend with chocolate. **99**

CHARLES DICKENS

💡 Chocolate was introduced into the United States in 1765 when cocoa beans were brought from the West Indies to Dorchester, Massachusetts.

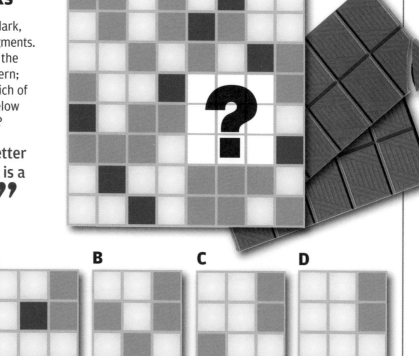

A   **B**   **C**   **D**

Shaping Relations

By examining the relationships of the following shapes, can you identify the next shape?

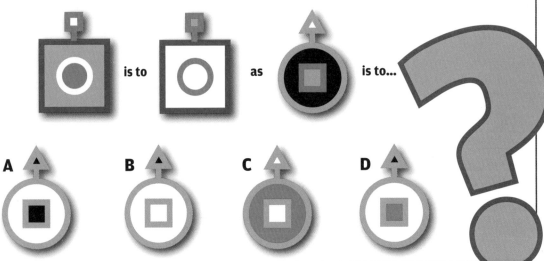

is to ... **as** ... **is to...**

A   **B**   **C**   **D**

How Many Bricks?

Assuming all blocks that are not visible from this angle are present, how many blocks have been removed from the cube?

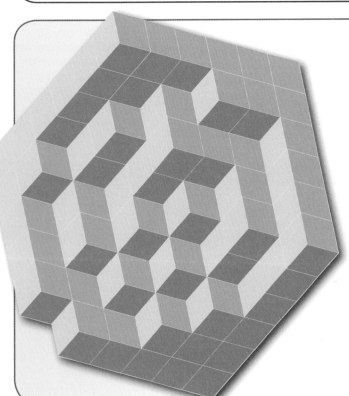

❝Better to be a strong man with a weak point, than to be a weak man without a strong point. A diamond with a flaw is more valuable than a brick without a flaw.**❞**

WILLIAM J. H. BOETCKER

Spin of the Wheel

The roulette ball is dropped into the wheel at the 0 section. When the ball falls into a number, 15 seconds later, it has travelled at an average speed of four metres per second clockwise, while the wheel has travelled at an average two metres per second in the other direction. The ball starts rolling 50 centimetres away from the wheel's centre. Where does it land? Take pi as having a value of exactly 3.2.

❝Every man is rich or poor according to the proportion between his desires and his enjoyments. ❞ SAMUEL JOHNSON

💡 The odds of winning roulette are slightly better if playing in Europe rather than North America. The US version has two zero spots versus Europe's one, cutting your chances of the jackpot from one in 37 to one in 38.

Solitary Letter

All these letters appear twice in the box except one. Can you spot the singleton?

❝Time is my greatest enemy. ❞ EVITA PERON

💡 The Rosetta Stone, the key to deciphering Egyptian hieroglyphs, was made out of granite.

Stars, Suns & Moons

Work out which number is represented by which symbol, and fill in the question mark.

> **The sun and the moon and the stars would have disappeared long ago... had they happened to be within the reach of predatory human hands.** HENRY ELLIS

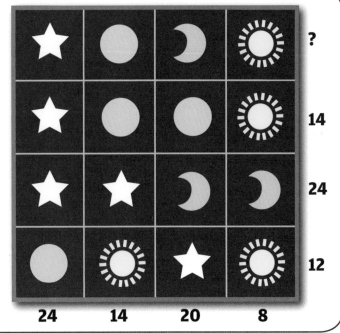

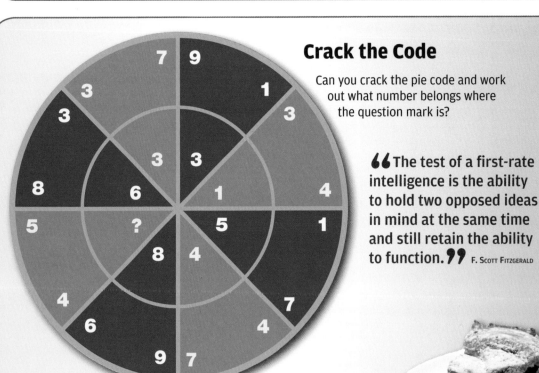

Crack the Code

Can you crack the pie code and work out what number belongs where the question mark is?

> **The test of a first-rate intelligence is the ability to hold two opposed ideas in mind at the same time and still retain the ability to function.** F. SCOTT FITZGERALD

The term "as American as apple pie" has its roots in England. The Pilgrims brought their pie-making skills, along with apple seeds, to North America. As the popularity of apple pie grew, the phrase was used to symbolize America and its growing prosperity.

Baffling Boxes

The shape below can be folded to make a cube. Which of the four cubes pictured below could it make?

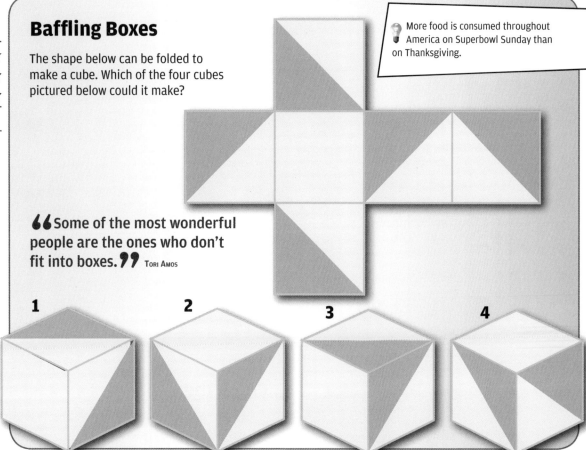

More food is consumed throughout America on Superbowl Sunday than on Thanksgiving.

66 Some of the most wonderful people are the ones who don't fit into boxes. 99 TORI AMOS

1

2

3

4

Logical Locations

Can you crack the logical secret behind the distances to these great cities, and work out how far it is to Melbourne?

66 Words are but the signs of ideas. 99 SAMUEL JOHNSON

The 1956 Olympics in Melbourne, Australia, were the first to be held in the southern hemisphere. The equestrian events actually took place in Stockholm, Sweden, because Australia had strict animal quarantine laws.

MOSCOW 78

BRASILIA 16

MELBOURNE ?

TORONTO 140

LAGOS 60

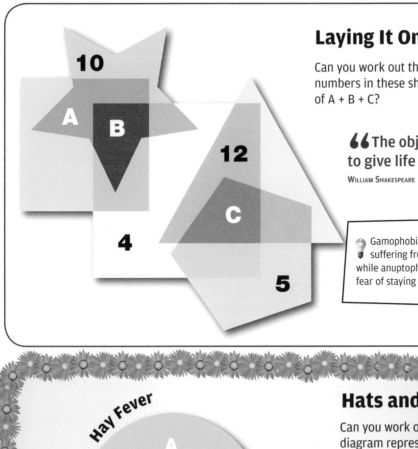

Laying It On

Can you work out the logic behind the numbers in these shapes, and the total of A + B + C?

❝The object of art is to give life a shape.❞

WILLIAM SHAKESPEARE

💡 Gamophobia is the term for anyone suffering from a fear of marriage while anuptophobia is the extreme fear of staying single.

Hats and Hay Fever

Can you work out which areas of this diagram represent women florists who wear hats but don't suffer from hay fever, and hay fever sufferers who wear hats but don't sell flowers?

❝No money is better spent than what is laid out for domestic satisfaction.❞

SAMUEL JOHNSON

💡 Australia is one of the countries worst affected by hay fever with up to 40 percent of its population affected during the season.

X and O

The numbers around the edge of the grid describe the number of X's in the vertical, horizontal and diagonal lines connecting with that square. Complete the grid so that there is an X or O in every square.

💡 The safety razor was successfully brought to market in the USA by King Gillette in 1901.

❝I have friends in overalls whose friendship I would not swap for the favour of the kings of the world.❞ THOMAS A. EDISON

Look to the Stars

Can you spot the 10 differences between this pair of pictures?

❝I don't know whose hand hung Hesperus in the sky, and fixed the Dog Star, and scattered the shining dust of heaven, and fired the sun, and froze the darkness between the lonely worlds that spin in space.❞

GERALD KERSH

💡 A basic mix-up between imperial and metric units has been cited as the cause of NASA's 1999 embarrassment when its $125 million spacecraft, the Mars Climate Orbiter, burnt up as it left the earth's atmosphere.

If all the DNA in your body was put end to end, it would reach to the sun and back over 600 times (100 trillion times six feet divided by 92 million miles).

Climb the Mountain

Can you reach the summit by replacing the question marks with numbers so that each pair of blocks adds up to the block directly above them?

❝My dear friend, clear your mind of can't.❞

SAMUEL JOHNSON

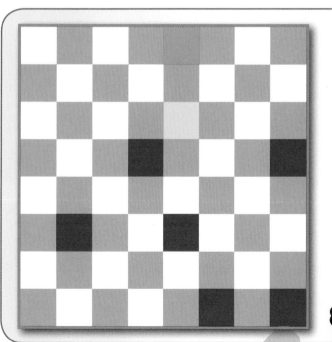

| ? |
?	?
?	?	?
?	40	?	11
?	?	?	?	?
6	?	11	?	2	2

Make Your Move

Can you place a queen, a bishop, a knight and a rook on this chessboard so that the red squares are attacked by exactly two pieces, the green ones by three pieces and the yellow ones by four pieces?

St Adrian Nicomedia is the patron saint of arms dealers, old soldiers and butchers. He is also a protector against the plague.

Floor Filler

Below is a plan of an apartment, and some very oddly shaped pieces of carpet.
Can you arrange them to fill the floor?

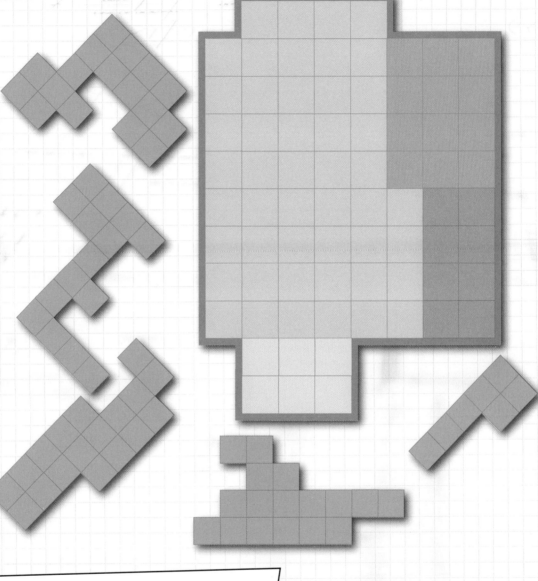

It is believed that Stonehenge was built in three separate
phases between 3000 and 1500 B.C. Experts suggest
that the construction of the ancient site required over
30 million hours of labour.

**66 It takes an endless
amount of history to make
even a little tradition. 99**

HENRY JAMES

Number Chunks

Divide up the grid into four equally sized, equally shaped parts, each containing numbers that add up to 36.

❝Mathematics is the only science where one never knows what one is talking about nor whether what is said is true.❞ BERTRAND RUSSELL

The grid (rotated, diamond orientation):

8
2 2
2 8 2
2 2 2 4
4 3 8 6 4
2 3 5 1 8 1
1 5 1 7 3
5 1 3 3
8 3 3
9 4
9

💡 Sir Isaac Newton instigated a Royal Society investigation to prove that he invented calculus before German mathematician Gottfried Wilhelm Leibniz, who had, in fact, published the method first.

Biggest to Smallest

Can you put these shapes A, B, C and D in size order, from biggest to smallest?

❝Each generation imagines itself to be more intelligent than the one that went before it, and wiser than the one that comes after it.❞ GEORGE ORWELL

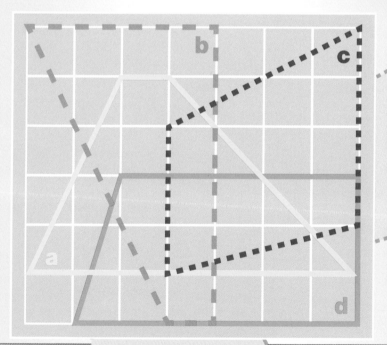

💡 The world's biggest airport is the King Khalid in Riydah, Saudi Arabia, which takes up 81 square miles.

Price Puzzle

At a medieval antiquities sale at Chateau D'Argent, you took 30,000 Euros, bought 18 items and spent every single cent you had. How many of each item did you buy?

> **"History is the witness that testifies to the passing of time; it illumines reality, vitalizes memory, provides guidance in daily life, and brings us tidings of antiquity. "** Marcus Tullius Cicero

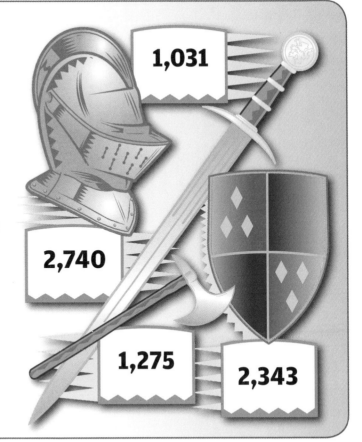

1,031

2,740

1,275

2,343

Destination Unknown

The directions below describe a route that connects two of the five houses below, and passes through every square on the map that isn't occupied by a house. Which two houses does it join?

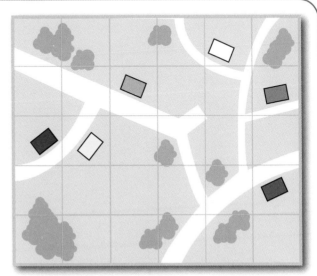

On 13 September 1899, Henry Hale Bliss became the first person to be killed by a traffic accident in the United States. He was struck by an electric-powered taxicab as he stepped down from a streetcar in New York City. The spot at West 74th Street and Central Park West is today marked by a plaque.

2D 5R 2U 2L 2U 3L 2R 4D 2R 3L 2R 3U 2D
3L 4R 3L 1R 1U 2R 1U 4L 1R 1U 2D

Fill Up!

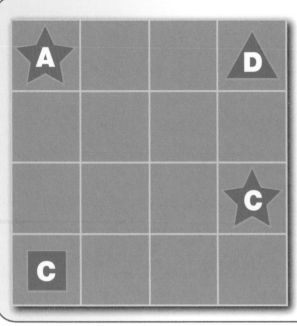

Fill up the shuffle box so that each row, column and long diagonal contains four different shapes and the letters A, B, C and D.

❝I not only use all the brains that I have, but all that I can borrow.❞ WOODROW WILSON

💡 Wheat is the world's most widely cultivated plant. It is grown on every continent except Antarctica.

Fold and Cut

Which of the patterns below is created by this fold and cut?a

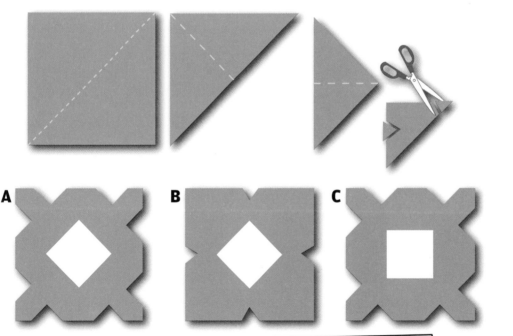

A   **B**   **C**

💡 An amateur astronomer named William Herschel first spied Uranus through his home-made telescope on 13 March 1781. It was the first expansion of the solar system in modern times. His observations helped to double the known size of the solar system and he was honoured by King George III.

Missing Dots

How many dots should there be in the hole in this pattern?

❝We should take care not to make the intellect our god; it has, of course, powerful muscles, but no personality.❞

ALBERT EINSTEIN

💡 Of an estimated 13-14 million species of animal in the world, 1.75 million have been recorded.

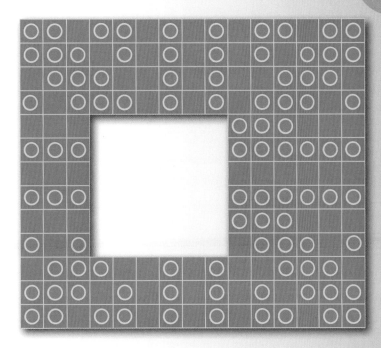

Tricky Trucks

Which toy box contains exactly the right parts to make the truck?

A 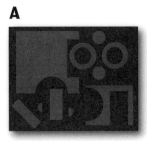 **B**  **C**

💡 The United States Postal Service operates the largest civilian vehicle fleet in the world with more than 216,000 vehicles driving more than 1.2 billion miles each year and using nearly 121 million gallons of fuel.

Perfect Symmetry

This picture, when finished, is symmetrical along a vertical line up the middle. Can you colour in the missing squares and work out what the picture is of?

💡 The Peregrine Falcon is the world's fastest animal. It has been known to reach speeds of 200 mph during near vertical dives in pursuit of prey.

Silhouette

Which of the coloured-in images matches the silhouette?

❝History will be kind to me for I intend to write it.❞

WINSTON CHURCHILL

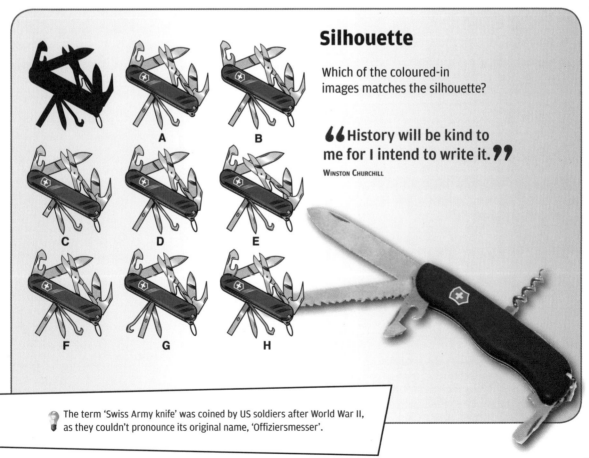

A

B

C

D

E

F

G

H

💡 The term 'Swiss Army knife' was coined by US soldiers after World War II, as they couldn't pronounce its original name, 'Offiziersmesser'.

Seeing Stars

Believe it or not, none of these stars is exactly alike. They represent every single combination of five colours - except one. Can you work out the colour placements on the missing star?

💡 Sirius is the brightest star in the night sky. Aptly named, the word comes from the Greek *seirius*, meaning, 'searing' or 'scorching'. Blazing at a visual magnitude of -1.42, it is twice as bright as any other star in the sky.

Easy as Pie

Can you crack the pie code and work out what number belongs where the question mark is?

❝Love conquers all things – except poverty and toothache.❞ MAE WEST

💡 An English soccer goalkeeper at the start of the twentieth century, William 'Fatty' Foulkes is thought to have been the first player to be on the receiving end of the popular football fans' terrace chant 'Who ate all the pies?'

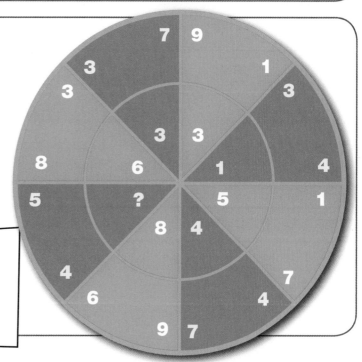

Symbol Sums

These symbols represent the numbers 1 to 4. If the green phone represents the number 3, can you work out what the other colour phones are representing and make a working sum?

+

+

=

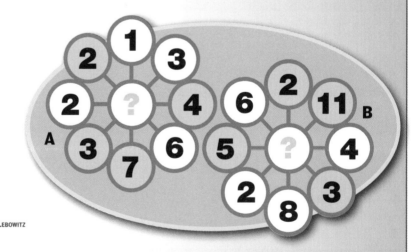

💡 The two key innovators of the Cubist art movement were Pablo Picasso and Georges Braque. Both were residents of Montmartre, a district of Paris.

Hubble Bubble

What numbers should appear in the hubs of these number wheels?

❝Wealth and power are much more likely to be the result of breeding than they are of reading.❞ FRAN LEBOWITZ

💡 Galaxies are classified using Edwin Hubble's scheme describing spiral, barred spiral, elliptical, peculiar and irregular shapes.

Going in Circles

Draw a single continuous line around the grid that passes through all the circles. The line must enter and leave each box in the centre of one of its four sides.

Black Circle: Turn left or right in the box, and the line must pass straight through the next and previous boxes.
White Circle: Travel straight through the box, and the line must turn in the next and/or previous box.

💡 In the late 1980s, scientists developed a draughts-playing computer programme. In 2007, they announced that the programme had been improved to the point where it was unbeatable.

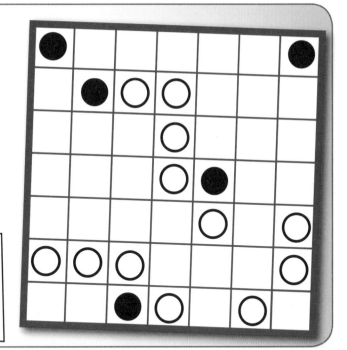

Compass Capers

Complete the grid by drawing an arrow in each box that points in any one of the eight compass directions (N, E, S, W, NE, NW, SE and SW). The numbers in the outside boxes in the finished puzzle will reflect the number of arrows pointing in their direction.

❝Conscience is a man's compass. ❞ Vincent Van Gogh

💡 The first magnetic compass was made in China during the Qin dynasty (221–206 BC). Fortune tellers used lodestones (a mineral composed of an iron oxide which aligns itself in a north-south direction) to construct their fortune telling boards. Eventually someone noticed that the lodestones were better at pointing out real directions, leading to the first compasses.

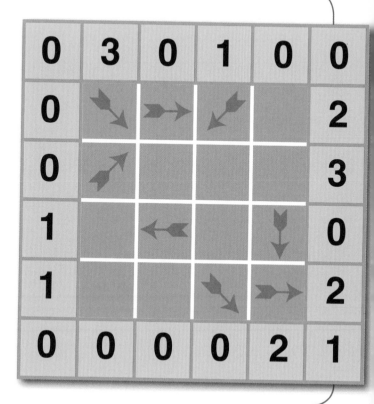

Fish Tank Thinker

Divide up the grid into four equally sized, equally shaped parts, each containing one of the five coloured fish.

❝If you want to catch more fish, use more hooks.❞ GEORGE ALLEN

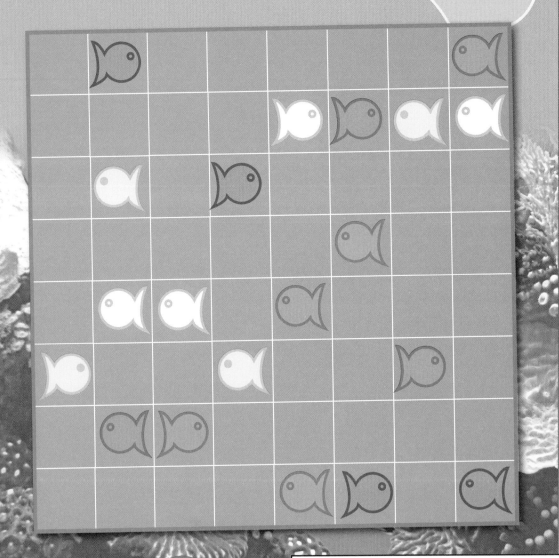

💡 Japan boasts 15 percent of the world's global fishing catch, which explains why sushi is so popular there.

Find the Pirate's Plunder

The numbers on the side and bottom of the grid indicate occupied squares or groups of consecutive occupied squares in each row or column. Can you complete the grid so that it contains two amulets, two cutlasses, two bars of gold and two keys, and the numbers tally?

66 Why join the navy if you can be a pirate? **99**
STEVE JOBS

2
1 1 2
6
1 1
1 1 1
1 1
1 2

1 1 3 3 2 2 1
5   1 2 1

Amulet   Cutlass

GOLD
Gold   Key

Blackbeard, perhaps the most notorious pirate in history, was eventually tracked down to Ocracoke Inlet, North Carolina, by the Royal Navy and killed in a brief but bloody battle on 22 November 1718.

In the Area

Can you work out the approximate area that this elephant head is taking up?

"Nature's great masterpiece, an elephant – the only harmless great thing." JOHN DONNE

100mm

Pack It In

Fill up the shuffle box so that each row, column and long diagonal contains four different shapes and the letters A, B, C and D.

"As human beings, we are endowed with freedom of choice, and we cannot shuffle off our responsibility upon the shoulders of God or nature. We must shoulder it ourselves. It is our responsibility." ARNOLD J. TOYNBEE

💡 In 1993, the world's first bicycle lift opened in Trondheim, Norway, to help cyclists negotiate the city's fearsomely steep Brubakken Hill.

DIFFICULTY ☆ ☆ ★

Gridlock

Look at the pattern to the right; which of the squares shown below correctly completes the grid?

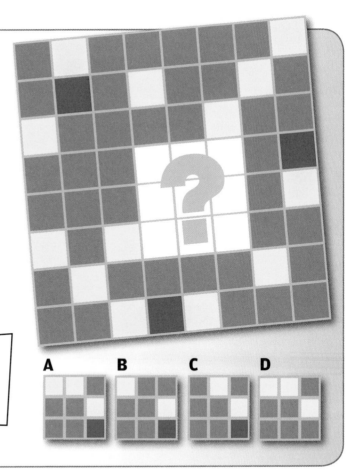

66 My wife and I, we like to ride where there's not much traffic. **99** Evel Knievel

💡 As of October 2007, the five most gridlocked cities in the USA are: New York City, San Francisco, Seattle, Minneapolis and Miami.

A   **B**   **C**   **D**

DIFFICULTY ★ ★ ★

Thinking Box

The value of each shape is the number of sides each shape has, multiplied by the number within it. Thus a square containing the number 4 has a value of 16. Find a block of four squares (two squares wide by two squares high) with a total value of exactly 70.

💡 When a hurricane has had a major impact, any country affected by the storm can request that the name of the hurricane be 'retired'. It cannot be reused for at least 10 years, to facilitate historic references, legal actions, insurance claims and to avoid public confusion.

Secret Colour Code

The pattern on the left gives you all the clues you need to colour in the pattern on the right. Can you work out the secret of the colour code?

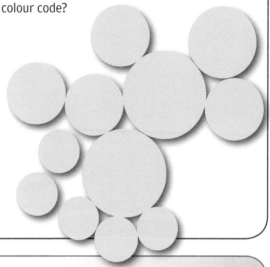

Dicey Directions

Each colour represents a direction – Up, Down, Left and Right. Starting in the middle die of the grid, follow the instructions correctly and you will visit every die in turn once only. What's the last die you visit on your trip?

Blue = Left
Green = Right
Yellow = Up
Red = Down

❝ Thinking is the hardest work there is, which is probably the reason why so few engage in it. ❞ HENRY FORD

SOLUTIONS

1: Flintlock Freddy is pirate E.

2:

3: B. Each row and line in the grid contains four black and four green squares.

4:

4	9	2
3	5	7
8	1	6

5: The rug is made up of 50 squares: 6 blue, 10 green and 34 yellow. Double these numbers to reveal a percentage breakdown of: blue 12%, green 20% and yellow 68%.

6:

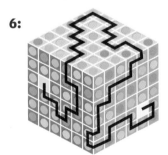

7:

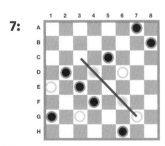

8: F.

9:

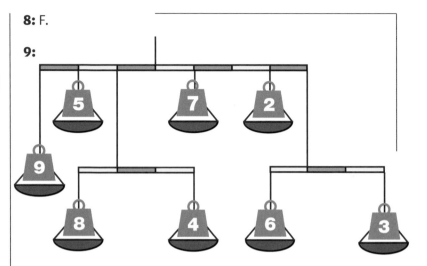

10: Each vertical and horizontal line contains one central square that is red, one that is green and one that is white. Each line also contains one top centre square that is black. Finally, each line has two images with brown squares top left and bottom right and the opposite squares in green, and one image where these positions have been reversed. The missing image should have a green central square, a black top centre square and the top left and bottom right squares in green.

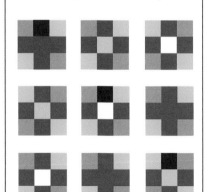

11:

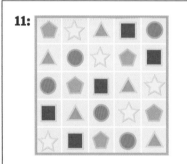

12:

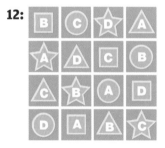

13:

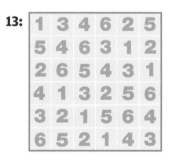

102

14:

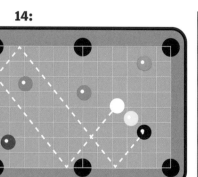

15: F is the odd one out.

16:

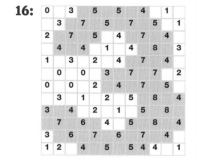

17:

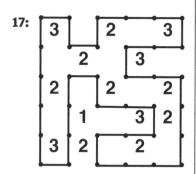

18: 25. Multiply the bottom two red corners and subtract the top two from your total.
8 x 5 = 40. 40 - 9 - 6 = 25.

19:

20:

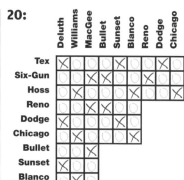

21:

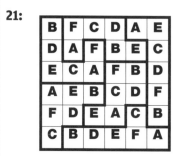

B	F	C	D	A	E
D	A	F	B	E	C
E	C	A	F	B	D
A	E	B	C	D	F
F	D	E	A	C	B
C	B	D	E	F	A

22: ?=18 (4+4+5+5=18).

	1
	4
	5
	9

23: Second tile on the bottom row.

24:

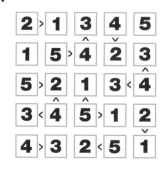

25:

26:

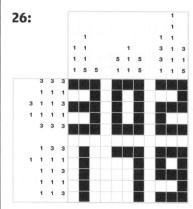

27:

28: 4.

29: A) 6. Add opposite numbers and multiply the integers of the total.
B) 12. Multiply the opposite numbers, then multiply the integers of the total.

30:

1	2	6	9	7	8	5	3	4
8	4	7	1	3	5	2	9	6
3	5	9	6	4	2	1	7	8
9	6	1	8	5	3	7	4	2
7	3	4	2	1	6	9	8	5
2	8	5	7	9	4	6	1	3
4	1	2	3	6	7	8	5	9
6	7	3	5	8	9	4	2	1
5	9	8	4	2	1	3	6	7

31: F and H are the pair.

32: If its bordering squares (not diagonals) are predominantly black, a square becomes black. If they are predominantly white it becomes white. If the bordering cell colours are equal in number, the square becomes yellow and if the bordering squares have now become predominantly yellow, a square also becomes yellow.

33:

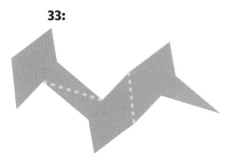

34: B. The blue dot and the blue square move one square anti-clockwise around the pattern with each new picture.

35: C.

36:

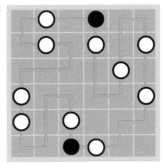

37: A, C, D and G.

38: A, C, D and G. B, E, F and H.

39: 60.

40:

41:

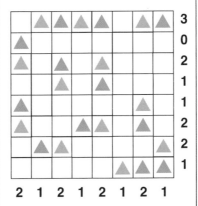

42:

43: 4. Subtract the right face from the front face and multiply by the top one.

44: A and F.

45: Add the top two corners, then add the bottom two. Then multiply the two totals. 3 + 1 = 4. 8 + 2 = 10. 4 x 10 = 40.

46:

47: A yellow square. Two different shapes are followed by a yellow shape. Two different coloured shapes are followed by a square.

48:

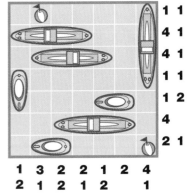

49: A yellow square. Every row and column in the grid contains three yellow and three red shapes, and the sides on the shapes in each row and column should add up to 24.

50: Each pentagon contains numbers that add up to 25. The sides nearest adjoining pentagons also contain the same number.

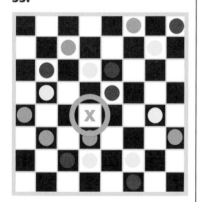

51: A. Each row and line in the grid contains three green, three red and one yellow square.

52: B, C, D and H.

53:

54: A) 15. Multiply opposite numbers, then subtract the yellow one.
B) 18. Halve the yellow numbers and multiply by their opposite number.

55:

C	F	B	A	D	E
A	B	D	E	C	F
B	E	F	D	A	C
F	D	A	C	E	B
D	C	E	B	F	A
E	A	C	F	B	D

56:

2		3		2			1
			2		2	3	
	4	1		1			3
			1			5	
4		4			3		
		6			3		3
				5			
1	3		4			2	0

57:

2	2		2	3
	3	1	2	
2				2
3	2		3	
3	1	2		2

58: Each vertical and horizontal line contains one shape with all green triangles, one with all pink triangles and one with half pink and half green triangles. Each line also contains two shapes with a white dot in the centre and one with no white dot. The missing shape must have all green triangles and a white dot.

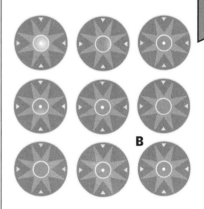

B

59:

18	13	14
11	15	19
16	17	12

60:

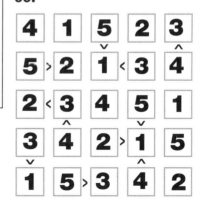

4	1	5	2	3
5 > 2	1 < 3	4
2 < 3	4	5	1
3	4	2 > 1	5
1	5 > 3	4	2

61:

1	7	9	2	8	6	5	4	3
2	5	6	9	3	4	8	7	1
4	8	3	1	5	7	2	9	6
7	2	5	3	6	9	4	1	8
9	6	8	4	2	1	3	5	7
3	4	1	5	7	8	9	6	2
6	9	7	8	4	2	1	3	5
5	1	2	7	9	3	6	8	4
8	3	4	6	1	5	7	2	9

62: [nonogram solution showing "358 787"]

63: Yellow.

64:

3R	3D	2D	1L
2D	OPEN	1L	3L
1R	2D	1R	1U
1U	2R	2U	1D
4U	4U	1U	1L

65: [logic grid with headers: Hellmuth, Chan, Brunson, 100 Dollars, 250 Dollars, 375 Dollars, Full House, Four Kings, Ace Flush; rows: Mac, Jack, Zac, Full House, Four Kings, Ace Flush, 100 Dollars, 250 Dollars, 375 Dollars]

66: A.

67: A black letter 'A'. Each row and column contains 1, 2 and 3 of each letter and each colour.

68:

		178			
	98		80		
	53	45	35		
27	26	19	16		
11	16	10	9	7	
2	9	7	3	6	1

69: D. The two outer shapes exchange colours, and the inner shape's colour and outline colour are also exchanged.

70: Blue = 1, Green = 2, Yellow = 3, Red = 4, Purple = 5. Three red balls are required.

71: ?=16.

[fruit puzzle: banana = 2, orange/kiwi = 3, grapes = 4, apple = 5]

72: The car is made up of 50 squares: 2 grey, 4 blue, 16 black and 28 red. Double these numbers to reveal a percentage breakdown of: grey 4%, blue 8%, black 32% and red 56%.

73: F11, L6, P14 and I6.

74: B.

75:
1. 2.
2. None.
3. 2.
4. Blue.
5. Green.

76: A. Each block of nine squares has been turned 90 degrees and the bottom left and top right symbols have been swapped over.

77: 5,250 square millimetres. Each 20 x 20 square represents 400cm². 8 squares, 3 half-sized triangles, 4 half squares, 3 quarter squares and 11 8th triangles are used.

78: A yellow number 4 on a pink background.

79: Up.

80:

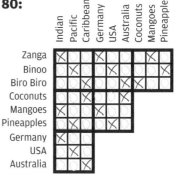

81: An orange star on a black circle. Two different coloured circles are followed by an orange star. Two stars the same colour are followed by a black circle.

82:

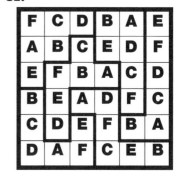

F	C	D	B	A	E
A	B	C	E	D	F
E	F	B	A	C	D
B	E	A	D	F	C
C	D	E	F	B	A
D	A	F	C	E	B

83: 66.

84:

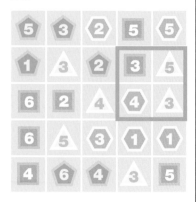

85:

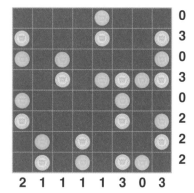

86: A, C, F and H.

87:

88:

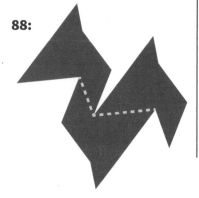

89: Each vertical and horizontal line contains one shape the right way up, one rotated through 90 degrees and one rotated through 180 degrees. Each line also contains one green shape with a blue outline and two yellow shapes with a red outline. The missing shape should be the right way up, and yellow with a red outline.

90:

1	7	3	2	8	5	6	4	9
5	9	8	1	4	6	2	7	3
2	4	6	3	7	9	1	5	8
4	1	5	9	6	8	3	2	7
6	2	7	4	1	3	8	9	5
3	8	9	5	2	7	4	1	6
7	6	1	8	5	4	9	3	2
8	3	2	7	9	1	5	6	4
9	5	4	6	3	2	7	8	1

91: 32 percent. The total number of items is 350, which, divided by 3.5 makes 100. The hat production of 112 when divided by 3.5 gives us 32, or 32 percent.

92: Purple.

93:

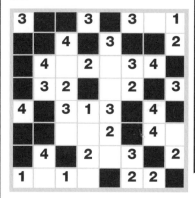

94: Hoss McGrew is cowboy A.

95: A green question mark.

96: Brown = 1, Black = 2, Green = 3, Blue = 4, Yellow = 5. Five black sacks are required.

97: ?=22.

3
4
5
8

98:

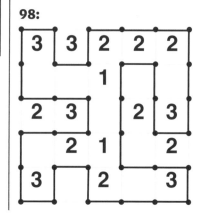

99: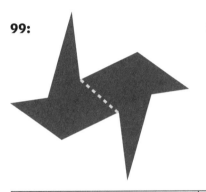

100:

101: 32. Using opposite corner stars, subtract the smaller number from the larger. Then multiply the two totals together:
9 - 1 = 8, 7 - 3 = 4, 4 x 8 = 32.

102:

103:

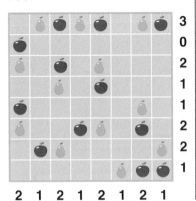

104: A blue circle. Two shapes the same are followed by a blue shape. Two different coloured shapes are followed by a circle.

105: C.

106:

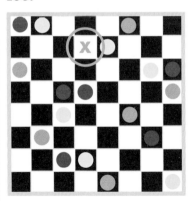

107: C and E.

108: Tokyo.

109:

	Taurus	Orion	Capricorn	Red Dwarf	White Dwarf	Neutron	East	West	North
Ipson 7	✗	○	○	✗	○	○	○	✗	○
Jalafrey 2	○	○	✗	○	○	○	○	○	✗
Zan 10	○	✗	○	○	○	✗	✗	○	○
East	○	○	○	○	✗	○			
West	○	✗	○	○	○	○			
North	✗	○	○	○	○	✗			
Red Dwarf	○	○	✗						
White Dwarf	✗	○	○						
Neutron	○	✗	○						

110: Both. Pythagoras tells us that the square of the hypotenuse is equal to the sum of the squares of the other two sides on a right angled triangle. The diagonal of the box floor is then 5 metres long (4 x 4 = 16, 3 x 3 = 9. 9 + 16 = 25, the square root of which is 5). This diagonal forms the base of a new right angled triangle with a hypotenuse 5.8 metres long, leaving enough room for both pieces of mast.

111:

112: E is the odd one out.

113: A line on the left or bottom of this square will give up just one box to your opponent.

114: Two-and-a-half revolutions of cog A, which will make exactly 4 revolutions of cog B and 5 revolutions of cog C.

115: D. With each new image, the colours of the parts of the car change as follows: Wheels - old cap. Cap - old top. Top - old bottom. Bottom - old door. Door - old wheels.

116:

117: Red = 1, Purple = 2, Green = 3, Blue = 4, Yellow = 5. Two blue balls are required.

118: A, C, D and G. B, E, F and H.

119:

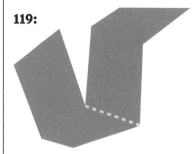

120:

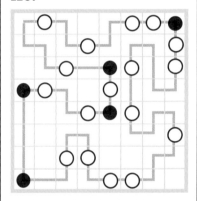

121:

8	7	9	6	1	4	2	5	3
1	2	4	3	5	9	6	7	8
5	6	3	7	8	2	1	4	9
2	1	6	9	3	7	4	8	5
4	3	8	5	2	1	9	6	7
7	9	5	8	4	6	3	1	2
9	4	1	2	7	5	8	3	6
6	8	7	1	9	3	5	2	4
3	5	2	4	6	8	7	9	1

122: A black letter 'A'. Each row and column contains 1, 2 and 3 of each letter and each colour.

123: 35 - 7 ÷ 4 - 4 = 3.

124:

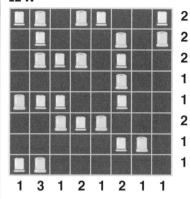

125: A and F.

126:

127: C, D, E and H.

128:

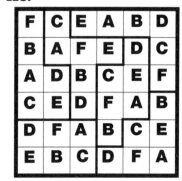

129: Down.

130:

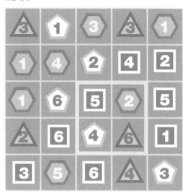

131:

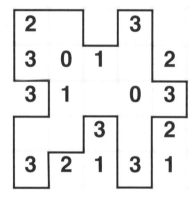

132: B is the odd shape out.

133: A pink triangle. Two shapes the same are followed by a pink shape. Two different coloured shapes are followed by a triangle.

134:

3	4	3	4	5	4	4
5	X	O	X	X	X	6
4	O	X	O	O	X	3
2	O	O	X	X	O	6
5	O	X	X	O	X	3
3	X	O	O	X	O	4
4	5	3	5	4	5	3

135:

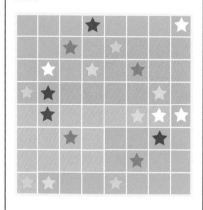

136: D. Each row and line in the grid contains four dark blue, three light blue and one pink square.

137: D. The two outer shapes exchange colours, and the inner shape's colour and outline colour are also exchanged.

138: 75.

139: In the 7 space.
The ball travels at a speed of 6 metres per second (relative to the wheel) for 15 seconds, making a distance of 9,000 centimetres in a clockwise direction. The circumference of the wheel is 320 centimetres (2 x pi (3.2) x radius (50cm)). The ball must then travel exactly 28.125 laps of the wheel (9,000 divided by 320 = 28.125), placing it one eighth of the way around the wheel in a clockwise direction, in the 7 space.

140: G.

141: 16.

142: The inner numbers are made up of the two outer numbers of the opposite segment, the smaller of which is subtracted from the larger. 4 - 3 = 1.

143: 4.

144: Take the alphabetical position of the first letter of the city, and multiply by the number of letters in the word. 13 (M) x 8 = 104.

145: 260. The numbers represent the number of sides in the shape they occupy. When shapes overlap, the numbers are multiplied. 40 + 160 + 60 = 260.

146: K and B.

147:

3	3	4	2	3	1
4	X	O	O	O	2
5	X	X	O	O	3
3	X	X	O	O	3
5	O	X	X	X	3
1	4	4	4	4	3

148:

149:

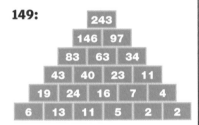

150:

151:

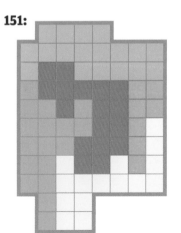

152:

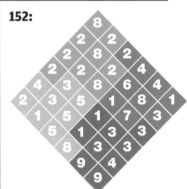

153: d) 16.5 a) 16 b) 15 c) 14.

154: 5 helmets, 5 shields,
6 axes and 2 swords.
5,155 + 11,715 + 7,650 + 5,480
= 30,000.

155: Red and yellow.

156:

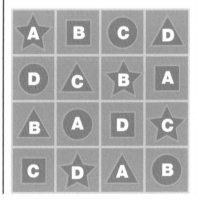

157: A.

158: 24.

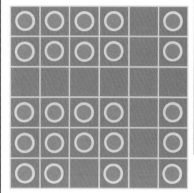

159: B.

160:

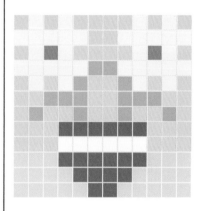

161: H.

162:

163: 1. The inner numbers are made up of the two outer numbers of the opposite segment, the smaller of which is subtracted from the larger. 4 - 3 = 1.

164: Yellow = 1, Red = 2, Green = 3, Blue = 4.

165:
A) 6. Multiply opposite numbers, then subtract the white one.
B) 24. Multiply opposite numbers, then add the white one.

166:

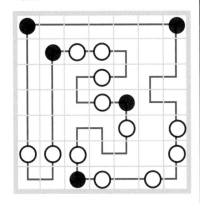

167:

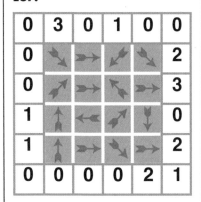

168:

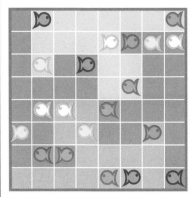

169:

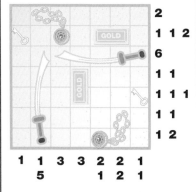

170: 5,100 square millimetres. Each 20 x 20 square represents 400cm². 8 squares, 4 half-sized triangles, 3 half squares, 4 quarter squares and 2 eighth triangles are used.

171:

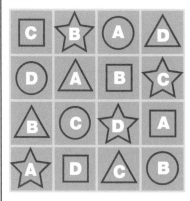

172: A. Each row and column in the grid contains two yellow squares, and every other row and column contains a red square.

173:

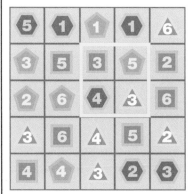

174: The colour of each circle is dependent on how many other circles it touches.

175:
The final dice in your trip is the yellow 2, four dice down in the centre column.